Animals at Bay

ANIMALS AT BAY
Rare and Rescued American Wildlife

Adrien Stoutenburg

Illustrated by John Schoenherr

Doubleday & Company, Inc., Garden City, New York

599
St

The author wishes to thank

the Chicago Zoological Park, Brookfield, Illinois,

the Committee for the Preservation of the Tule Elk, Los
Angeles, California,

the Defenders of Wildlife, Washington, D.C.,

the Department of Game and Fish, Santa Fe, New Mexico,

the Division of Wildlife Research of the Bureau of Sport
Fisheries and Wildlife, U. S. Department of the Interior,

and the Wichita Mountains Wildlife Refuge, Cache,
Oklahoma

for their cooperation in providing helpful information for
this book.

To the memory of that instinctive
conservator of earth and creatures,
my step-grandfather,
CHARLEY R. MINIER
1862–1948

Contents

Preface

A brisk May wind blew across the prairie grass, bending the tops into running troughs like ocean waves. The grass was so tall that it brushed against the bellies of two horses trotting over a plain near the Platte River in what is now Nebraska. On one horse was a young explorer from Boston, Francis Parkman. Although Parkman's clothes were stained from his travels by river boat, wagon, and horseback, they were still "citified" compared to those of the professional guide and hunter beside him. Instead of boots, Henry Chatillon wore scarred Indian moccasins, a white blanket-coat, and trousers of deerskin with long fringes at the seams. Both men carried rifles and hunting knives and scanned the vast, sky-mantled landscape with a common goal in mind: buffalo.

There had been many signs of buffalo at the travelers' camp by the river, though so far there had been no actual sight of the shaggy monarch of the plains. But there were other animals nearby to provide excitement. Above the grass tops, almost everywhere Parkman looked, were the peering black eyes of creatures that were called antelopes. Many, eager with curiosity, came so close that he could easily see their erect, pronged horns and white throats. Beyond, the hairy backs of wolves appeared and disappeared in the deep, blowing grass.

Parkman got down from his horse and practiced shooting at the wolves, while Chatillon kept searching the landscape for buffalo. At last, he cried, "Let us go!" and pointed toward two black specks slowly crossing the ridge of a distant sand hill. Parkman leaped back into his saddle and joined the guide in pursuit of the beasts.

After a short gallop toward the hills, the men found the land changing swiftly to bleak sand covered only with clumps of grass or harsh plants, at the same time that the sky darkened with clouds. The two buffalo disappeared, but a quarter of a mile distant, more appeared—a long line walking in single file. The animals were unaware of Chatillon who dismounted and began crawling across the ground toward them. He carried with him both his own rifle and Parkman's, the unskilled Parkman being left to hold the horses. Chatillon was out of sight when Parkman heard the sharp reports of the two rifles, one fired swiftly after the other.

Chatillon returned and he and Parkman rode up toward the crest of the hill where the buffalo had been. There lay the two beasts, rifle balls through their lungs. In the dusk, with a storm beginning to lash the gorges and ravines, Parkman struggled clumsily to help the guide carve the choicest parts of meat from the two dead animals. He admired and envied the older man's skill, and dreamed of the day when he would be able to bring down his own buffalo.

Some days later, on another buffalo hunt, Parkman was separated from the guide and his other companions on the expedition, when he went riding off in pursuit of a huge buffalo bull. He managed to force his horse within six or eight yards of the galloping beast, so close that he could almost smell the sweat-blackened back, and see the moisture of the tongue that lolled nearly a foot from the creature's jaws. Just as he was about to aim his pistol, the bull slowed, turned, and lowered its great head to charge. Parkman's horse reared in terror. The bull wheeled, fleeing again, and Parkman's pistol shot went wild. Before he could even think about reloading his weapon, the bull had vanished.

Frustrated and tired, Parkman reined his panting horse and looked around for some landmark that would guide him back to the camp. He realized that he might as well be looking for a landmark in the middle of an ocean. All around him stretched the prairie, rolling and treeless from one horizon to the other. Deciding that the Platte River should lie to the north, he consulted the compass hanging around his neck, and started off. He rode for two hours, seeking some glimpse of the river, but all he saw was a wild landscape without a sign of human life. He knew that Pawnee Indians could be hidden behind distant slopes and ridges, but if so, they were as invisible as his traveling companions. Nevertheless, he was not alone. The land teemed with animal life.

"The face of the country," he wrote in his famous book, *The Oregon Trail,* "was dotted far and wide with countless hundreds of buffalo. They trooped along in files and columns, bulls, cows, and calves, on the green faces of the declivities in front. They scrambled away over the hills to the right and left; and far off, the pale blue swells in the extreme distance were dotted with innumerable specks. Sometimes I surprised shaggy old bulls grazing alone, or sleeping behind the ridges I ascended. They would leap up at my approach, stare stupidly at me through their tangled manes, and then gallop heavily away."

Mixed in with the buffalo, more accurately known as American bison, were the antelope-like creatures now called pronghorns. "The antelope were very numerous," Parkman recorded. "They would approach to look at me, gaze intently with their great round eyes, then suddenly leap aside, and stretch lightly away over the prairie, as swiftly as a race-horse. Squalid, ruffian-like wolves sneaked through the hollows and sandy ravines. Several times I passed through villages of prairie dogs, who sat, each at the mouth of his burrow, holding his paws before him in a supplicating attitude, and yelping away most vehemently, whisking his little tail with every squeaking cry he uttered . . . Various long checkered snakes were sunning themselves in the midst of the village, and demure little gray owls, with a large white ring around each eye, were perched side by side with the rightful inhabitants."

He rode on through a "vast congregation of brute forms," and finally decided to follow a buffalo trail in the hope that it would lead him to the river where the buffalo came to drink. He had made a wise choice, and soon the river glistened ahead of him. A few wolves glided by, butterflies fluttered about his horse's head, and multitudes of lizards darted under its hoofs.

Parkman arrived safely back at camp. He and his companions traveled onward toward Fort Laramie in Wyoming. Beyond Laramie, Parkman saw still more prong-horns, buffalo, prairie dogs, and wolves. There were rattlesnakes, too, one as thick as his arm. White-tailed jack rabbits, some almost two feet long, leaped across the trail. These western hares were twice the size of the cottontail rabbits Parkman had seen in the east. In one spot, two hundred elk came out of a meadow, their antlers clattering as they walked close together. Overhead, curlews gave their screaming cries, and eagles soared. In the mountains, trout and beaver splashed in streams and ponds, while the prints of deer, bighorn sheep, foxes, coyotes, mountain lions, and grizzly bears crisscrossed the land.

The amount of game Parkman saw on his 1846 journey from St. Louis, Missouri, to Wyoming, and then back through Colorado and Kansas, seemed unlimited. Yet he had seen only a portion of the wilderness. West of the Rocky Mountains stretched vast deserts, valleys, forests, and coast mountain ranges—and the ocean. Everything brimmed with various kinds of animal life. At the Pacific's edge, innumerable sea otters tumbled among the kelp beds, while fleets of gray whales made their yearly migrations up and down the coast. Great numbers of grizzly and black bears roamed the country. In one year's hunting season, in 1848, five trappers returned from the Oregon Territory with seven hundred grizzly bear pelts. Still, it was the prairies and plains that was the greatest game country in the New World, bustling, humming, and rampant with animals ranging in size from the burly bison to tiny rodents.

When Christopher Columbus arrived off America's shores, bison roamed from New York to Oregon and into Canada and Mexico. Well before Parkman's time, the bison had retreated from their eastern ranges, the last one east of the Appalachian Mountains being killed in Pennsylvania on January 19, 1801. Today there are no wild bison anywhere except for a few free roaming herds transplanted to Alaska, and in the Wood Buffalo Park in North Alberta and the Northwest Territory.

And who, today, has ever seen two hundred wild elk come clattering out of a mountain meadow, or even one plains wolf streaking after pronghorn or deer? Of the multitude of prairie dog villages, how many remain? And where are the giant grizzlies, the bighorn sheep, and the once abundant giant blue whales?

Even though wildlife seemed boundless in Parkman's time, some species had already disappeared completely under the pressure of hunters and settlers. It is estimated that around one hundred different animal species in the world have become extinct, mostly at the hands of human beings. Many of the surviving species are still seriously threatened, in the United States and in other countries. Over one hundred years have elapsed since Parkman set out on his journey. In another hundred years, what animals will peer at a traveler from the grass or forests, what tracks will cross wilderness trails? The number and variety will depend on what is done today to preserve what is left of America's wild heritage.

1   Pacific Gold

Rain turned to sleet and snow, and the men on board the battered Russian ship, the *St. Peter*, wondered if they would ever see the shores of Siberia again. Driven by wind, the ship's sails ragged, they feared they might never again see land of any kind. Behind them was the Alaskan coast, and though they had known the triumph of discovering it, the price had been a horrible one in human suffering. Even the Captain Commander, Vitus Bering, was too weak to leave his cabin. Hardly a day went by without one or more of the crew dying, while the little ship blundered for weeks through a long, broken chain of barren and rocky islands.

The islands were the Aleutians, and the *St. Peter* was one of two ships that had left the Siberian coast in June, 1741, to explore the dangerous and then uncharted northern seas. Unknown to the Captain Commander, the sister ship had also reached Alaska and was laboring homeward. In July, the *St. Peter* had reached its goal, the American mainland. Now, three months later, the *St. Peter* was trapped in the increasingly stormy waters of what is today called the Bering Sea.

By November, the island chain was behind the ship, with only snow-lashed waves ahead. Almost without hope, the lookout stared through the mists and wind. Then, on

November 4, he sighted a distant, looming shadow. Land!
The lookout shouted the news and the sick and the dying
crawled on deck to see the miracle. Some of the stronger
seamen carried Vitus Bering out of his cabin to look at
what everyone believed was the Siberian home port.

Sheathed in ice, the little ship crept forward through a
bitterly cold night. In the morning a fresh gale sent torn
ropes and broken tackle smashing to the deck. Waves beat
the already cracked timbers of the ship. Anchors were put
down but the cables ripped apart. Drifting helplessly, the
St. Peter finally smashed against the rocks of what turned
out to be a group of uninhabited islands, the Commanders,
a hundred miles from Siberia.

There was barely time to get the men ashore before the
ship broke into jagged, floating pieces. One of the crew
members riding a careening landing boat to safety was a
German naturalist, Georg Wilhelm Steller. As the landing
boat drew near an adjacent island, he and his companions
saw strange, lively herds of animals swimming toward them.
In spite of the rough water and slashing spray, the creatures
leaped, rolled, and dived with ease. Steller had noticed
the strange animals earlier, along the coast of Alaska and in
the Aleutian Islands, but he had not had the opportunity or
interest to look at them closely. Watching them as he neared
the island, he thought their acrobatics were like those of
monkeys, and he decided to call them "sea apes." More
important to his companions as well as to himself, the sea
animals meant food.

When the crew had found shelter in dens and caves,
they set about killing the "sea apes," which congregated
in beds of seaweed all around the island, and on the edge
of the rocky shore. The wide-eyed, cheerful-looking creatures had little fear of men, never having known human
beings before, and were easily killed with a club or a rock.

The crew killed them by the dozens and then by the hundreds, first for their palatable flesh and then for their beautiful fur. Even though the Russian sailors shivering in fox dens had little hope of ever reaching home, they began to hoard the thick silky furs while they dreamed of the riches such furs might bring.

For nine months, the shipwrecked Russians were confined to the bleak islands. Bering died in December, and the island where he died now bears his name. The survivors managed to build a crude boat from the wreckage of the *St. Peter* and in August, 1742, they put to sea. With them they took eight hundred pelts of the strange aquatic creatures they had discovered. Thirteen days later they arrived home to be stared at by friends and relatives as if they were ghosts. But traders and trappers stared at the soft, rich pelts the explorers had brought back. The fur was even more luxurious than that of the Russian sable— and the sable was growing scarce from overhunting. Here, in its place, was this new creature which the returned adventurers said was so abundant there seemed no end to its numbers.

As soon as ships and crews could be got ready, Siberian hunters started out to harvest this new, valuable source of fur. It was the beginning of an era of a hundred years during which Russia ruled Alaska and extended its influence along three thousand miles of the coast of North America, as far south as California.

The animal which so affected the course of history was the sea otter. This otter is the largest member of the weasel family, which includes the river otter, mink, wolverine, and many others. Long-bodied, with a broad, whiskered snout and small ears, a grown otter may measure up to five feet in length, and weigh as much as eighty pounds. The front paws are small, webbed, and stubby; the large rear feet are webbed and resemble furry flippers, the claws just visible. It is these flippers that make the sea otter so fast and powerful a swimmer that it can outrace almost any other swimming animal, although it is sometimes captured by killer whales and sharks. The sea otter can dive three hundred feet or more, cleaving its way through buried rock crevices and slipping through forests of seaweed. There it can remain for as many as four minutes before surfacing for air.

One of the sea otter's special traits is its playfulness and good nature. When it is not sporting in the surf, playing hide and seek, or hunting food, it spends its time lazily floating on its back, its paws tucked against its chest, its flippers and stubby tail curled upward against its belly. Very often, an island of kelp makes a soft mattress for the dozing otter, and in stormy weather he may wrap strands of the kelp around him to keep him from drifting off beyond the security of the kelp bed; sharks and killer whales balk at pursuing the otter into this green-brown, slippery jungle. The sea otter can float in a vertical position, too, like an elongated brown cork, and he often does this when an enemy is near, only the top of his head and his bulging black eyes visible. At such times, he often lifts a paw and shades his eyes· from the sun, peering under his "palm" like a human being. Another characteristic that gives the sea otter a seemingly human quality is that he is one of the few mammals to use a tool. Favorite foods on his menu include fish, crabs, cuttlefish, clams, and spiny sea urchins. Some of these have hard shells that are difficult to open or break. The sea otter solves the problem by diving to the ocean bottom where he clutches a flat rock in his paws. Back on the surface, he turns over and places the rock on his chest or stomach. Then he bangs the shellfish upon the rock until it cracks open.

A female sea otter is one of the most affectionate mothers in the mammal kingdom. Baby sea otters are usually born in April or May, their coats grayer than those of their brown-furred parents. They are born with their eyes open and a full set of tiny teeth. Even so, they nurse for a year or more, and are not fully grown for four years though they may breed at three years. The mother otter with a young cub or kit carries him around and nurses him while she floats on her back. In case of danger, she tucks him under her arm and dives into the kelp. Stories are told that when a baby is killed, the mother refuses to leave the spot, whimpers in grief, and sometimes even forgets all about eating and so dies of sorrow and hunger. But when there is no threat to her or her cub, she spends much of her time teaching him to swim, dive for food, and play. When there is a convenient reef nearby, she drags the youngster onto it and there fusses over him, licking out any snarls in his coat, like a cat with kittens. Unlike a cat, she usually has only one youngster to worry about. Nor does she spend all her time petting him and caressing him. If the cub is slow about learning what he should do to succeed in his watery world, she gives him a cuff or two until he does learn, regardless of how he may complain.

What made the sea otter so special to the early Russians, however, and to the English and Americans later, was the quality of its fur. The fur is thick and soft, varying from reddish brown to almost black, stippled with silver-gray guard hairs. Unlike the fur of other animals, which becomes thin or shaggy from shedding at certain parts of the year, the sea otter's coat is always "prime," meaning that it is in top condition.

A band of sea otters is called a pod, and when the Siberian hunters first sailed through the stormy Aleutian waters where some seven hundred islands stretch for over

a thousand miles, they found numberless pods of what came to be called "swimming gold." Uppermost in the hunters' minds was the thought of the money they could make from the skins. Sea otter pelts were in great demand, especially among Chinese mandarins, and the royalty of Russia.

One of the first Russian expeditions to visit the island where the *St. Peter* had been wrecked, returned home with the pelts of sixteen hundred sea otters, plus four

Sea otter

thousand of blue foxes and fur seals—$90,000 worth of furs. During the crew's year-long stay in the area, they lived chiefly on the flesh of another newly-discovered animal called a sea cow.

The sea cow had first been seen by the scientist, Georg Steller, during the 1741 voyage. The cow was a giant creature, twenty-five to thirty feet long, and weighing up to four tons. Steller described it as being not a seal, nor a whale, but something in between. Hunters had a comparatively easy time harpooning the slow-moving mammal as it grazed on the grasslike seaweed among shoreline rocks, and when the hungry sailors sampled its flesh they found that it tasted like fine beef. No one knows just how many of the odd creatures there were—Steller was the only person ever to leave a written description—but within thirty years after its discovery, Steller's sea cow was extinct.

The only American relative of this species is the manatee or sea cow which ranges from Beaufort, North Carolina,

along the Florida coast, and west through the Gulf of
Mexico and the islands of the Caribbean Sea to Latitude
20°S in South America.

In 1745, another and larger expedition set out from
Siberia. Reaching the Aleutian Islands, the group prepared
to organize a landing party, only to see a hundred or more
savage-looking natives standing on the beach, armed with
spears and wearing long shirts made from sea otter pelts
and birds' skins. The Russians murmured uneasily among
themselves, fingering their muskets, and then finally went
ashore in a landing boat, ready to shoot at the first sign of
trouble. Almost the moment they stepped on shore, the
natives came forward, looking more shy and curious than
threatening. The Russians offered presents of tobacco and
pipes, and the Aleuts gave a carved stick in return. Curiosity
got the best of one native and he tried to take a musket from
one of the men. A fight broke out, and the leader of the
landing party ordered his companions to fire. The Aleuts

Sea cow

fought back as best they could and the Russians fled to the landing boat.

Blood had been shed, but it was only a trickle compared with what was to come. By barter or trickery, the Russian visitors took all the sea otter pelts the Aleuts had on hand; then, wanting more, they forced the native hunters to go out in their light, narrow canoes and procure others. The Aleuts in their skin-covered boats, built with round openings that fit so closely around their bodies that the craft and the occupant seemed one, were far more skillful than the

Russians at killing the sea otters. On the Commander Islands the otters had made easy targets for they had clustered on shore, but Aleutian otters had learned that it was safer to stay out in the floating kelp and watery reefs. There the clumsy landing boats of the Russians were no match for the swift animals. The Aleuts, canoes encircling the creatures in a "spearing surround," were a match not only for them but even for whales and seals.

The Aleuts did not hunt willingly for the Russians. It took blows, curses, and even murder, before they submitted. By the time the Russians left, the natives on Attu Island had almost been wiped out.

More and more vessels set off for the New World and returned with bundles and bales of pelts. Even so, none had repeated Bering's trip as far as the mainland, which the Aleuts called *Al-ay-ek-sa*, although there were rumors that it was a treasure chest of natural riches. For the time being there were riches enough in the Aleutian Islands, ship after ship returning home with cargoes of fur. One ship came back with three thousand otter skins, and over four thousand of fox. Many others returned with similar cargoes. In 1763, one adventurous captain pushed his ship as far as what is now Kodiak Island. Several of the natives, in their kayak-like canoes, ventured out to look at the strange wooden vessel with its two masts. It was the first ship of any kind that they had seen and they thought it was a huge whale. After watching the men on the ship smoking, seeming to put fire in their mouths and blow smoke out, the natives decided that the ship was a monster carrying devils. Although that ship moved on to another bay, it was on Kodiak Island that the Russians were to establish their first colony in what is now a part of the United States, Alaska.

Gradually, the Russians reached the Alaskan mainland,

dreaming of a new Russian empire built upon the fabulous
fur of the sea otter. The once great herds in the Aleutian
Islands were thinning out, so that the hunters had to press
farther eastward. In the meantime, ambitious and daring
merchants and sea captains had made fortunes in rubles,
while the sea otters died from spears, guns, nets, and clubs.
As many as 150,000 pelts were taken in a two-year period.
There was no thought among the hunters of sparing female
otters with cubs so that new adult otters would replace
those killed. Ruthlessly, indifferent to the future, they killed
every sea otter they could, and then sought for more. Russian leaders dreamed of claiming all of America and they
sent their ships on ever-widening routes. Spaniards, who
had already claimed California, sent their own expeditions
northward up the coast, fearing the encroachment of the
Russians. They, too, were familiar with sea otters, for the
animals appeared off the rocks of the Pacific Coast, at what
is now San Francisco, and at Monterey.

Soon the English also were involved. In 1778, two English
ships under the command of Captain James Cook anchored
in a large bay on the west coast of Canada's present
Vancouver Island. Canoes filled with natives rowed to the
ship. Among the gifts the natives brought were the skins
of various animals, chiefly those of the sea otter. The officers
and crew admired the soft elegance of the otter fur, but
they had no idea of its value. Further north, in Prince
William Sound and Cook Inlet on the Alaskan coast, the
explorers found the waters thick with sea otters and were
given still more pelts by the friendly natives, as souvenirs.
The Englishmen treated the furs almost as rags. The velvet-
soft pelts ended as padding in bunks, or were tossed into
damp lockers where they began to smell and some were
finally dumped overboard. It was only later, after the death
of Captain Cook on the Hawaiian Islands, where he was

killed by natives in February, 1779, that the English realized what a precious cargo they had on board. The two ships, under a new captain, made a short stop in China. Several Chinese merchants learned that there were sea otter skins aboard, and at once offered sums for them that seemed fantastic to the English. Sailors and officers hunted up every pelt or scrap of a pelt, and the Chinese eagerly paid even for the ragged ones. A good pelt brought $120– yet the natives of the American coast and islands had given them away in exchange for beads and trinkets. The seamen on board were so excited that they almost mutinied in their desire to go back to Alaskan waters and hunt the sea otter themselves. Even the captain was tempted. However, the ships sailed back to England. There, in 1784, the journal of the expedition was published. The "secret" was out, and the English, like the Russians before them, began readying ships and crews for the Northwest coast where diving, swimming, dark-eyed creatures could be changed by rifle ball and spear into a fortune.

It was not long before Americans, too, began to catch the scent of gold from the sea otter trade. In the fall of 1787, two Yankee ships left Boston to make their way on the long voyage around South America's Cape Horn and on up the Pacific, with Alaska's Nootka Sound as their destination. The captains, John Kendrick and Robert Gray, imagined that they would be the first traders in the area, but when they arrived they found that the sea otter trade was already a source of conflict between Russia, England, and Spain. Each nation schemed and fought for dominion. The Russians pushed southward, claiming territories for their Empress. The Spanish hustled northward from Mexico, asserting the rights of the King of Spain, while the English put in their claims for Great Britain's King George. Now the United States flag was added to the scene. Captain

Gray, in the *Columbia,* was the first American to carry the new nation's flag around the world, unloading a rich harvest of sea otters in China before returning safely to Boston.

When New England merchants saw the silks, spices, and teas that Gray had brought back from the Far East in exchange for sea otter pelts, they were in a fever to increase such trade with China. New expeditions were hastily prepared, and Gray set out again for the Northwest coast. Exploring southward from Nootka, in the spring of 1792, he entered the mouth of a great river which he called the Columbia, after his ship. Because of this, the United States later claimed ownership of the area.

Although the Americans had been latecomers to the sea otter trade, they quickly moved to the forefront. In the year that Gray sailed into the Columbia River, there were twenty-eight ships on the Northwest coast, and most of them flew the United States flag. In the meantime, the coastal waters were increasingly flecked with sea otter blood. Nobody knows exactly how many otters died under the continual onslaught, nor how many skins were bundled into ships' lockers, but it is known that millions of dollars were made and that the harvest was one of the richest in the whole history of the fur trade. In most places, the natives would still trade the beautiful pelts for beads or other cheap trinkets. For such rewards, plus rum and firearms, or under threats of punishment, they slaughtered one herd after another. Before the men in great, white-winged ships had come, the natives had killed no more sea otters than they needed for clothing or food. But then all was changed and neither they, nor the white hunters, seemed to realize or care about the fate of the species.

The slaughter went on, as did the rivalry between the fur traders. As late as 1812, Russia still clung to its dream

of conquest in America, and in that year started a settlement in California less than one hundred miles north of
San Francisco. The restored remnants of this colony, Fort
Ross, still stand in the form of weathered gray stockades,
blockhouse, and chapel. Only the ghosts of the hopeful
colonists remain. The Russian colonizers found very few
sea otters, and their attempts at shipbuilding and agriculture failed. By 1838, increasing numbers of Americans began to push into the area, challenging the presence of the
Russians. The Spanish, then in possession of California,
were equally hostile. Eventually the Russians gave up, and
in 1841 sold all their holdings to a Swiss immigrant, John A.
Sutter. This was the same Sutter on whose land in the
Sacramento area of California, gold was found seven
years later, an event which started the famous California
gold rush.

The Russians were having troubles northward along the
coast, too. The sea otters in the areas under their control
were at last beginning to thin out. In Cook Inlet, where it
had been easy to gather three thousand pelts in a hunting
season, it took considerable work to get even a hundred.
And the native hunters, the Aleuts and Kodiaks, were no
longer a source of skillful slave labor. They were dying
out from diseases brought by the white men. Those surviving had lost the hunting and rowing arts of their ancestors, or had grown so bitter at the abuses and lack of
rewards for their toil that they no longer cared what the
white hunters said or did. By 1826, the Russians were able
to harvest only fifteen pelts from Unalaska, one of the
largest islands among the Fox Island group in the Aleutians. Still they managed to hold on until 1867. In that year,
the United States purchased Alaska, and it was the Americans' turn to invade the remaining sea otter breeding
grounds.

On the great plains of the American West, hunters were

busy slaughtering herds of bison. Now, on the Northwest coast, Americans in ships began killing the sea otter at a faster rate than the Russians had. They set out in large ships which carried Aleuts and their canoes. Wherever sea otters were found, the expedition commanders ordered the Aleuts into their canoes, gave them the latest make of rifles, and supervised the hunt. In spite of the dwindling numbers of sea otters, daring or lucky traders still could find enough here and there to make the rugged journeys successful. Then, year by year, it grew harder to find even small pods of sea otters. Ships that had once brought back several thousand pelts were lucky to return with two dozen.

By 1900, the sea otter, which had ranged over a five-thousand-mile semicircle starting near the north end of Japan, northward along the Siberian coast, along the Aleutian Islands, and down the western coast of North America to Lower California, had become so rare that only the high prices paid for pelts encouraged hunters to continue searching out the animals' last hiding places. By 1910, even the most determined traders gave up. They, and almost everyone else, believed that the sea otter had vanished forever. Although it appeared that there were no sea otters left to protect, the United States, Great Britain, Russia, and Japan signed a treaty in 1911 making the hunting of the sea otter illegal. The treaty was actually concerned mainly with protecting fur seals, another species that had been hunted near the point of extinction.

It seemed that protection of the sea otter had come too late. There were rumors that some had been seen off California's coast, or that poachers were still able to find a few in Alaskan waters, but even if these rumors were true, could such small numbers survive?

In 1936, the government organization, the Biological Survey (now known as the Fish and Wildlife Service), sent a scientific expedition to Alaska to find out the facts about the existence of sea otters. The scientists returned with the good news that the sea otter was not extinct. They had found the animals on six of the Aleutian Islands, forty-eight near one island, seven hundred at another. Then, in 1938, a headline in a California newspaper announced EXTINCT SEA OTTERS PLAY IN SURF. Photographers, reporters, and individuals who had never heard of the sea otter before, rushed to see what the creature looked like. There, in the kelp beds off Monterey, California, the mild, shining creatures that had played such an important role in the history of the United States and of the world, dived and somersaulted and floated as if guns and clubs had never existed. A mother otter swam peacefully nursing her cub, while the male otters snoozed or held mock battles. One otter dived through the kelp in search of food while another chewed at the contents of an abalone shell grasped in its stubby paws. The watchers on shore counted ninety-four sea otters. Twenty years later the Monterey colony had increased to some five hundred.

As of 1966, it was estimated that there were approximately forty thousand sea otters alive, and that their numbers were increasing. So strictly are they protected today that it is against federal law even to own a sea otter pelt without a special permit. Also forbidden is the capturing of live sea otters, so that there are none to be seen in zoos. Even though the sea otter is making a comeback, and occupies over twenty percent of its former range, its population is still very low. Whether it will continue to increase and spread depends on continued protection.

At the time that the sea otter was being killed by the tens of thousands, a distant cousin was fighting for its life thousands of miles away on the North Atlantic coast. This was the sea mink, a large, reddish-furred resident of the islands off the coast of Maine and the Maritime Provinces of Canada (New Brunswick, Nova Scotia, and Prince Edward Island). Early American colonists hunted the sea mink eagerly, for its fur. Among the sea mink's favorite haunts were the islands of Penobscot Bay. There, hunters with trained packs of dogs chased the creatures from island to island, searching any ledge where a sea mink might be hiding. If the sea mink crept into a rock crevice where the dogs could not reach it, the hunters used crowbars and shovels to pry him out. Sometimes the crevices were so deep that even crowbars could not reach the sea mink, but often the hunters could see the animal's eyes shining in the darkness. Then a careful shot with a rifle took care of the matter, the carcass being dragged out by a long rod with a screw in the end. If it was impossible to shoot the sea mink in his hiding place, the men fired charges of pepper into the narrow opening, or smoked the animal out with brimstone. Coughing, gasping for breath, the sea mink would usually try to reach fresh air, only to be seized by the waiting dogs or felled by a bullet.

The last of the sea minks was killed about 1860, less than two hundred years ago. Today all that is left of this vanished species are a few skeletal remains. No one in New England or Canada will ever open a newspaper carrying the good news EXTINCT SEA MINKS PLAY OFF SHORE! Although the sea mink, as far as we know, was the first mammal to become totally extinct in our country, other American mammals are reaching the danger point, or have disappeared altogether from the wilds.

2   The Big Hairy Ones

A tall, blue-eyed man walked cautiously along a game trail, his rifle ready for any wild game that might appear. Evidence of such game was all around in the form of tracks and droppings left by deer, elk, bison, pronghorns, and their faithful followers, the wolves.

Although the April shadows were cool, the weather was far more pleasant than it had been back in the Mandan Indian camp where the Corps of Discovery had spent the winter of 1804–1805. Captain Meriwether Lewis still shivered at moments when he remembered the freezing cold of those months on the upper Missouri River. Mostly, now, his mind was concerned with the future and the hope that his and Captain William Clark's plans for reaching the Pacific Ocean would not miscarry. If they were successful, they and their men would be the first to make a scientific exploration of the land all the way from the Mississippi River westward.

Lewis heard a crackling of twigs behind him and turned. It was one of the expedition members who had come with him on the hunt. He started to speak, then saw his companion stop and stare ahead. Lewis wheeled. Two bears faced him and the other hunter. They were not like the black bears he had often seen before. These were larger, with a kind of hump on their backs, the fur unusually thick and streaked with grizzled, silvery hair. Even as Lewis brought his rifle to his shoulder, he remembered all the warnings the Indians had given about the fierce "white bear." He and his men had glimpsed the bears earlier, but the animals had never bothered them. Lewis fired. Almost at the same moment, the other hunter's rifle cracked. One of the bears turned and fled. The other, blood streaming over its coarse hair, reared up, small eyes gleaming in fear and pain. Then it dropped to all fours and started toward Lewis.

There was nothing for Captain Lewis to do but run as he tried to insert another charge into the muzzle of his rifle. His companion, too, was frantically reloading his own weapon. For seventy or eighty yards, the bear pursued Lewis, but the animal was too severely wounded to run swiftly. With his rifle reloaded, Lewis stopped, turned, and aimed again. The rifle ball struck the beast but still the shaggy form managed to stay upright. The other hunter fired and the bear dropped, rolled over, and lay still.

The two men approached warily and studied the grizzly. He was not fully grown, but he weighed three hundred pounds, and the long tusks in his open mouth, the talons on his paws, were evidence that he was not a creature a man would want to come up against bare-handed.

A few days later, the Lewis and Clark expedition had another encounter with a grizzly bear, near what is now Wolf Point, Montana. Captain Clark and a fellow hunter were patrolling the area in the vicinity of the Missouri River where the expedition's canoes had landed for the evening, when they met the largest grizzly seen so far. Both men fired, their rifle balls whizzing home. The giant creature gave a roar, then turned and ran. The men fired again, once more striking the shaggy beast; and then again.

Five of the rifle balls passed through the bear's lungs, five more pierced other parts of his body. In spite of this, the bear reached the wide river, plunged in, and swam half-way across until he managed to struggle up onto a sand-bar. There he sprawled, still breathing, still defiant. At last, after about twenty minutes, he shuddered into stillness. According to the records of the expedition, the bear measured eight feet seven and a half inches long, and weighed an estimated five or six hundred pounds, at the least. (The average measure for grizzlies is from six to seven and a half feet. Some may weigh as much as 800 pounds.)

Until then, the captains of the expedition had made light of the Indians' stories about the power and stamina of the beast whom the Indians said walked like a man. After meeting such a large one, the explorers felt differently. Their journal of the famous trek records, "The wonderful power of life which these animals possess renders them dreadful; their very track in the mud or sand, which we have sometimes found 11 inches long and 7¼ [inches] wide, exclusive of the talons, is alarming; and we would rather encounter two Indians than meet a single brown bear." The explorers used "white" and "brown" and "yellow" in describing such bears but they meant the grizzly.

In what is now California, the grizzly was an all too common species, as far as the early Spaniards were concerned. Probably the first white men ever to meet a grizzly were the Spanish explorers, Cabeza de Vaca and his three companions, who explored the Southwest between 1527 and 1536. After them came other Spaniards—explorers, missionaries, and soldiers—who built forts and churches along the California coast from present day San Diego to north of San Francisco. The early Spanish and later the Mexicans killed the grizzlies for fear that the beasts would at-

tack their cattle or invade their ranches and vineyards, as they sometimes did. And, in spite of the bears' fierce reputation, the early Californians also used the creatures for sport. Riding swift horses, the *vaqueros* practiced lassoing the heavy-footed creatures and then dragged them home in triumph. During California's "Rancho Days" in the 1830s and '40s, the Spanish grandees invented still another form of sport involving grizzlies. In this they matched a captive grizzly against a bull.

Warm sunlight touches the red-tiled roof of the Mission San Luis Rey at the southern end of California, and lights up an adobe-walled quadrangle where a crowd has gathered behind the safety of a five-barred fence. The sun glances off the velvet jackets and glittering capes of the rancheros, and the gold and silver ornamented saddles of their horses. The colorful shawls of the women, the glinting, high combs in their dark hair, adds to the sparkle. By contrast, the large grizzly chained to a thick post in

Grizzly bear

the center of the quadrangle looks drab, though his size is impressive. For years, up until this year of 1830, he has been roaming the pine-clad slopes of Palomar Mountain high above the little mission. Trapped, imprisoned in a cage, he has been brought here for the afternoon's entertainment. He is a cattle killer, the rancheros say, and deserves to be punished. Now let him show what he can do against a long-horned bull!

The grizzly's hind feet are tethered by a rawhide reata which stretches about a yard between each foot. Another length of rawhide, fastened to the center of this bond, is attached to a center post. The bear tries to gnaw at the rawhide ropes but a man on horseback prevents this by heavy prodding with a long pole.

As soon as everything is ready, men at one side of the arena open a gate. A wild longhorn bull, lassooed for the occasion, comes snorting into the open, hoofs kicking up dust, eyes flashing. In his normal haunts, the bull would avoid his natural enemy, the bear, but now he is almost blind with panic and rage, ready to charge at anything that moves. He scarcely pauses and with the sharp, curved horns lowered, charges toward the grizzly. Those in the crowd who have placed money on the bear, gasp, certain that the grizzly must end up being tossed into the air. The bear rises with a seeming calmness, erect on his hind legs, waiting until the bull's horns are within a few feet of his chest. With perfect timing, his front paws lash out, powerful talons gripping the bull on each side of its head. A twist of the paws and the powerful head is turned, the muscular neck wrung, before bear and bull roll together in a snarling and snorting heap. Suddenly the bear is on his feet again, nimble as a dancer in spite of his weight. In front of him the bull lies motionless, its neck broken.

There are shouts of triumph from the bear's owners and

supporters. Four horsemen ride into the arena, being careful to avoid getting too close to the furious bear, and drag the vanquished bull out through a gate. The runway to the bull pen opens and another bull charges out, tasseled tail high, his glistening, twisted horns even longer than those of the first bull. Surely, this time, the horns will find their mark before the bear can dodge or seize them. But the grizzly does dodge, at exactly the right moment, the bull shooting past—but not quickly enough to avoid a crushing swat from one whacking paw. The crack echoes around the corral, together with the cries of the crowd. The bull plunges to his knees, one horn plowing up the dust. All hear the snap as the long horn breaks. His shaggy opponent strains against his bonds, trying to reach the fallen bull.

Fighting the ropes that hold him, the bear is taken off guard as the bull rises, wheels, and charges toward him again, his remaining horn aimed. The bear gives a roar as the horn slices through his shoulder, leaving a long gash, and turns on the bull with fresh fury. Again, the wheeling bull charges. This time the grizzly is ready. Now he grabs the bull's head, twisting it halfway around, while his jaws close on the bull's nose. Both animals roll over and over in the dust until the bull quivers into motionlessness. The grizzly stands up, triumphant, but he is weak now from his wound and is less steady.

That's enough, the bear's owners say, but the crowd has not had enough blood. Another bull! they chant. Another! Another!

Once more the gate opens. This time the bear is not so quick, and one of the bull's horns pierces the base of the grizzly's neck. Even so the bear manages to grab, seize, and twist, and there is a loud, familiar crack as the bull's neck breaks.

Another! chants the crowd. They know that the fiercest and strongest bull remains. It is unfair, the owners protest, for the bear is tired and badly wounded. The crowd jeers and fists shake menacingly; the owners give in. First, though, the bear is given a little more freedom in the length of the reata holding him, and is permitted to rest a moment. But he spends the minutes struggling desperately to chew away the imprisoning thongs. And now another bull charges toward him. Clumsily, the bear tries to twist the bull's head as before. He fails and another wound spurts red at the side of his thick neck. The two maddened animals roll together, dust swirling, people cheering the bull as they see the bear's new wound. Surely it is all over with the grizzly. But there he is starting to rise to his feet to meet the next charge. The bull hurtles forward even as the grizzly rears upward, still full of power and danger. He falters strangely. The reata has tangled around one of his hind feet so that he cannot get his feet planted solidly. Tripping, he falls forward, and one long horn pierces his breast. Still the grizzly struggles to rise, in spite of the blood pumping out of him. Once more he is on his feet, but the battle is hopeless. Another charge and the bear rolls over backward, killed at last.

Brutal performances like these were common in the days of the rancheros, and they continued through the times of the gold rush when bearded, red-shirted miners made up much of the audience. One of the last bear and bull fights took place at San Fernando Mission in the 1860s. When not hunted and captured for such fights, the grizzlies were shot for sport or killed by ranchers who considered them a menace to their livestock. The meat was not generally prized, although it was on the menu of the Eldorado Hotel in 1850, in what is now Placerville, California, once the main entrance to the gold fields. An old bill of fare reads: Grizzly roast, $1.50; Grizzly fried, $ .75.

In the 1860s the state of California paid a bounty of ten dollars for each grizzly scalp, and several hunters brought in more than a hundred scalps apiece in one year. The same kind of thing went on throughout the grizzly's whole range, which in frontier times included the Great Plains to the Pacific Ocean, and from Canada to Mexico. Exactly how many grizzlies there were is almost impossible to guess, but one authority estimates that there were at least 100,000 roaming the mountains, plains, and west coast as late as 1850.

With the exception of the brown Kodiak bear of Alaska, the grizzly is the largest of the carnivores (meat-eating animals) in North America. But he eats other food besides meat. He is omnivorous, eating anything, both animal and vegetable food. He is fond of berries, nuts, salmon, honey, and even ants, and will spend hours patiently fishing, or ripping apart an old log for the sake of finding tasty grubs. One of his chief sources of meat in the early days was bison, and he followed the bison herds, watching for his chance to pick up the weaker animals. Often, though, small rodents satisfied his hunger for meat.

For centuries the grizzly and the American Indian shared the wilderness. Although it was a mark of great courage for an Indian to kill a grizzly, the red men had a mystic respect for the mighty creature. Most Indian tribes believed that various animals were their ancestors. Among their animal heroes was the cunning coyote. But most admired of all was the mighty bear with whom they claimed relationship. From one coast to the other, from Quebec to California, various Indian tribes referred to the grizzly as "grandfather" or "grandmother." The Crees on the Plains called him a "four-legged human" or sometimes "chief's son." The Sauk Indians called him "old man," while the Blackfoot tribe called him "the big, hairy one." Whatever they called him, they built legends around the grizzly's strength, and held ritual dances in his honor. A necklace of grizzly bear claws was prized above all others for it took rare courage to obtain such an ornament. Against the grizzly's raking claws the Indians had only arrows, spears, and stone axes. Though several daring braves usually banded together to attack the furry giant, it was a perilous undertaking. Even when Indians acquired horses from the early Spanish conquistadors in the middle of the sixteenth century, they still were no match for the "white" bear.

"A bear is wiser than a man," the Indians said, "because he knows how to live all winter without eating anything."

This saying referred to the bear's custom of taking a long sleep during the winter in cold climates, usually from late fall to early spring, the length of time depending on weather and locality. He seeks out a natural den like a cave, scrapes together a bed of leaves and grass, and then curls up for his long snooze, from which he may rise occasionally if the weather is mild. Before settling down in this fashion, he has prepared himself for the months ahead when most of his food supply may be buried under snow or ice, by eating heartily. In the den, he draws the little energy he needs from the fat stored in his body.

In the case of a female grizzly, this ability to go without food or liquid is even more amazing because it is during this winter sleep that she bears her young. The cubs arrive two or three months before the mother leaves the den. Usually there are two cubs, but there may be only one, and rarely, four. The cubs are surprisingly tiny, weighing between one pound and one-and-one-half pounds each,

Grizzly bear

and measuring about nine inches in length. They are entirely helpless, their eyes closed, lacking teeth, and with so little hair that they look naked. By the time they follow their mother out into the springtime world, they are about the size of house cats. It takes several months before they are ready to forage food for themselves, and even when they begin to dig up roots or nibble tender grass shoots, they continue nursing their mother's milk throughout the summer. Even when they are a year old, they still travel with the mother bear. They are not fully grown until they are around eight or ten years old. During their first two years, or even in their third, they often spend the winter months in the same den with the mother.

The father bear is mostly notable for his absence. In fact, after a female becomes a mother, she appears to avoid not only the father of her cubs but all male grizzlies, although male bears do occasionally join the females and cubs in summer. Some authorities say that adult male grizzlies pounce on and destroy any cubs they come across, and this may be the reason why the mother usually avoids the males.

The grizzly bear normally lives longer than most other land animals. Outside of man, he has no important enemies —disease rarely attacks him. If he can avoid traps and bullets he may live anywhere from fifteen to twenty years. In a good zoo he may live much longer. His only weakness, as with all bears, is his poor eyesight. This is compensated for by an exceptionally keen sense of smell and hearing.

Largest of all bears are those which live on Kodiak Island off Alaska. The Kodiak bear, the largest carnivore in the world, stands sometimes ten feet tall; some that have been shot weigh fourteen hundred pounds. Up until the 1890s scarcely anyone knew about the Kodiak bear. Once he was discovered, hunters set out to add his pelt to their trophy displays. The bears were killed by the dozens and within thirty years the species faced extinction. Almost at the last minute, the United States government stepped in and gave the huge beast protection, in 1926.

The real threat to grizzlies began when American frontiersmen and settlers acquired fast-loading firearms that could deliver heavy charges. Along with the wagon trains rumbling westward in the 1850s, came the large caliber *Sharps* rifle. With this a marksman could deliver a heavy ball at comparatively long range. Just as white men once said, "The only good Indian is a dead Indian," they said, or believed, that the only good grizzly was a dead one. Whether the grizzly was a menace or not, the majority of the pioneers immediately raised their rifles at the sight of the shaggy beast. They seldom killed for the sake of food or fur, but chiefly for what they considered sport, leaving the animal to rot where it fell. Or, if an excuse was needed, they argued that grizzlies were fearsome man-eaters, that they would spring from the brush on unsuspecting women and children, or that they were bloodthirsty attackers of cattle.

There are records of grizzlies having attacked or killed human beings without any known motive, but in the great majority of cases the bears turned on their human enemies only when attacked or when they felt threatened. Most animals fight back only when they consider themselves in danger. Female animals with young are especially fearful for their offspring and are easily triggered into action, whether they happen to be bears or birds. A mother bear with cubs is easily excited and very protective. As for the killing of livestock, the grizzly bear was guilty of this at times, but he was not the complete criminal that stock ranchers made out. Yet, it was because of cattle, chiefly, that "Old Ephraim" as white men called the grizzly, was slaughtered to the vanishing point. The Spanish, pushing northward from Mexico, brought their herds of cattle with them. Later, pioneers from the east arrived on the Great Plains, and in the Southwest, with their droves of cattle and other farm stock. Very often cattle strayed and ended up shifting for themselves in the wilds, grazing on the vast, open ranges, mating, creating more of their kind until there were great herds. Slow moving, they were an easy prey for the grizzlies into whose territory they had wandered. As buffalo and other wild game disappeared before the white man's guns and traps, the grizzly turned to this new source of food. As human beings had discovered before him, beef was a tasty item. Unfortunately, the grizzly could not tell the difference between a wild steer and a domestic one. Both tasted the same to Old Ephraim but it was not the same matter to the stockmen.

Kill every grizzly in sight! was their slogan. Like an army, they marched out with guns, trained dogs, traps, poisons, and single-minded determination. Outnumbered though he was, and defenseless against human instruments of destruction, the silver-tipped bear was a crafty foe. Highly intelligent, increasingly cautious, he quickly learned to keep hidden as much as possible. Where once he had wandered freely in the open, he now sought the safer areas of rugged mountains and canyons. But there was no escape, and scarcely any mountain peak or cliff that the hunters could not reach.

Slowly and steadily, the great grizzly was driven back from the hills and plains where he had roamed at will. Ranchers and hunters paid less attention to the grizzly's smaller cousin, the black bear, although this smaller bear sometimes reached six hundred pounds or more. The so-called black bear has color phases ranging from brown to reddish cinnamon, and he is a generally easygoing creature with none of the fierce pride of the grizzly. Unlike the grizzly, the black bear can climb trees, a very useful skill when pursued by dogs. Although he might occasionally invade a farmer's pig pen, or attack a sheep, he was considered more of a nuisance than a menace. Neither Indian nor white man felt that the black bear was a challenge compared to the "ferocious" grizzly bear. Consequently, numbers of black bear survived even as the grizzly retreated.

Many a trapper, hunter, rancher, or sportsman gained fame for the number of grizzlies he managed to kill. President Theodore Roosevelt, who loved big game hunting and yet at the same time was interested in conservation, wrote frequently of his experiences in hunting grizzlies. To him the bear was "the King of game beasts . . . the mighty lord of the wilderness . . ." But by the time Roosevelt began hunting the grizzly, the great bear had already begun to change. He was no longer the lord of the wilderness. "Bitter experience has taught him caution," Roosevelt wrote. "He has been hunted for sport, and hunted for his pelt, and hunted for the bounty, and hunted as a dangerous enemy to stock, until, save in the wildest districts, he has learned to be more wary than a deer, and to avoid man's presence almost as carefully as the most timid game."

Even as Roosevelt wrote, in 1887, the great bears were diminishing so fast that their absence was not entirely a matter of avoiding men. Nineteen years later, the well-known zoologist, Dr. William F. Hornaday, published a warning. "In the United States, outside of Yellowstone Park and the Bitter Root Mountains, grizzly bears are now so rare that it is impossible for a sportsman to go out and kill one, no matter where he hunts, and no matter how much money he spends . . ."

Today, in California, the only grizzly to be seen, except for those in zoos, is on the state's Bear Flag. Once common in Arizona's White Mountains and along the upper branches of the Blue River, no grizzly bear has been seen in the state for many years. It was reported that one was killed in 1936, but this is unproven. If true, it was probably the last of the Arizona grizzlies. The last grizzlies known to have lived in New Mexico were killed in the mid-1930s. In Utah, the latest record of a wild grizzly was made in 1923, and considerably earlier in North Dakota. The story is the same throughout the western states; the Fish and Wildlife Service lists the grizzly bear, *Ursus horribilis*, on its list of endangered American animal species. "An endangered species," according to this Service, "is one whose prospects of survival and reproduction are in immediate jeopardy . . . An endangered species must have help, or extinction will probably follow."

Only in Alaska and Canada are there grizzlies in any abundance. These, plus a few which have sought refuge in Glacier and Yellowstone National Parks, and a handful in Idaho, Wyoming, Montana, and possibly Colorado, are all that are left of the "king" of the wilderness. For years the grizzly was given no protection whatever from hunters. Even today, in states where a few straggling grizzlies survive, there are open hunting seasons, and each year several grizzlies accused of being stock killers are taken by government trappers.

Approximately 850 grizzlies remain in the United States south of Canada. Alaska remains the grizzly's best hope. Hunting is allowed but only one bear per hunter is permitted, and it is against the law to shoot a female bear with cubs, or the cubs themselves. The skins of bears must be shown to a representative of the Game Department for inspection and approval before they can be taken elsewhere. In 1965, the brown-grizzly bear kill in Alaska was 825. How many grizzlies are there in the state of Alaska? The Alaska Department of Fish and Game has guessed that there may be ten thousand or more, most of them concentrated in the remote wilderness areas as in the Selkirk Mountains, and the Yukon and MacKenzie territory, Kodiak Island, and the Alaska Peninsula. Even though hunting is controlled, poachers remain a threat. And as Alaskan cities and highways develop, who can be sure that these surviving grizzlies will not be pushed back to the vanishing point as has already happened in the rest of our states below the Canadian border? Admiralty Island, only twenty miles from the city of Juneau, has an estimated one brown grizzly per each of its sixteen hundred square miles, the most populous bear habitat in the world today. But commercial logging there, permitted by the United States Forest Service, is dooming those bears. The national wildlife refuge on Kodiak Island, the home of the brown Kodiak bear, is also threatened. Cattle owning residents of the island have recommended that the bears be exterminated to protect their cattle.

Laws help but do not always mean complete protection. In June, 1966, a two-hundred-pound male black bear appeared on the outskirts of a suburban town near Kansas City, Missouri. The moment the news was out, men ran to get their guns. By the time a state conservation agent arrived, he found over one hundred armed persons surrounding the frightened bear.

"The first one who shoots him gets the hide!" one of the men said.

The agent looked nervously from one to the other for it appeared that the excited men might start shooting each other over the bear—or shoot the agent if he tried to enforce the Missouri Wildlife Code which prohibits killing bears unless they are molesting livestock—a very unlikely possibility with the black bear who is primarily fond of vegetation or insects. And this black bear had bothered no one.

The agent reluctantly authorized the bear's destruction because of the danger of armed human beings shooting wildly at each other. "The suburbs of a major city is no place for a bear," he admitted, "but I wish it could have been allowed to live."

In spite of such incidents, the black bear is still present in many parts of its original range, though most numerous in the Rocky Mountain area and the Northwest. In Yellowstone Park black bears are a nuisance because visitors insist on feeding them or carelessly leave garbage accessible, in spite of rules against it. Tame though these bears have become they are not pets and it can be a dangerous business to ignore the park signs which say, PLEASE DO NOT FEED THE BEARS. Semi-tame animals are almost always more dangerous than those in the wild.

Far to the north, the polar bear of the Arctic regions is being hunted to the edge of danger. Of the twenty-five largest polar bears known in the records of big game hunters, fourteen have been killed since 1960. Once it was quite a feat for a hunter just to reach the frigid areas where the white bear lives; he had to travel long days by ship and then by dog sled to reach his prey. Today, the hunter can hop into a morning jet plane in New York City and be at Anchorage, Alaska, in time for supper. There, a local plane takes him to the next stop where a guide arranges the hunt. The airborne hunter and his friends take off, fly low over

the ice floes where polar bears live, and discharge their high-powered weapons into the helpless forms below, before landing to claim the pelts.

The increase of military and weather posts in the Arctic, including Alaska and Canada, is another threat to the disappearing polar bear. The majority of new men stationed at the posts want to obtain a bear pelt to take home with them, to show off their hunting prowess.

In 1965, nearly four hundred polar bears were killed in Alaska alone. Over a thousand were killed in Canada, Greenland, and the Norwegian Arctic, even though there are regulations against indiscriminate hunting. There are closed seasons during which no polar bears may be hunted in Alaska, and in hunting season special permits must be acquired. Russia outlawed all hunting of the species in 1956. Canada allows only Indians, Eskimos, and a small group of licensed hunters to hunt the species. Greenland and Norway, too, have restrictions but as late as 1966 a

Norwegian travel agency tried to lure tourists to Norway by guaranteeing them a chance to shoot their own polar bear.

Polar bears, like grizzlies, breed slowly. In the wild, a female may give birth to one or three cubs, though usually two, every second year. In zoos—there are many in zoos—they breed more frequently. But there is a great difference between a caged animal and one that is free. Not only is an animal in the wild an exciting thing to see, but each animal plays an important ecological role, meaning that it contributes to the over-all balance of nature.

Polar bears do not live on the north polar ice cap. They are carried around the pole constantly on the great masses of drift ice and into the seas of northern Siberia, Scandinavia, Greenland, and Alaska. The bears never remain in one national territory or territorial waters for long. Because of this, they can never be fully protected except by agreement among the countries involved. A step toward this was made when in the fall of 1965, five countries, including the United States and Russia, met to study the problem. The future of the wild polar bear—and other bears—depend upon such efforts, and upon the cooperation of commercial hunters and sportsmen. Private companies cater to these hunters and sporting magazines carry advertisements offering the services of guides and outfitters to help the hunters bring down the game animals. However, not all sportsmen are indifferent to the preservation of dwindling species. A famous organization, the Boone and Crockett Club, founded by President Theodore Roosevelt, removed the polar bear from its eligible list of trophy game animals in 1966, although certain other species of increasingly rare animals such as the grizzly, the mountain lion, and the bighorn sheep, remained "fair game." On the other side of the scale, the Alaska Big Game Trophy Club decided in

1967 to add the wolverine to its list of big game animals for record competition—though the fearless, secretive wolverine, no larger than a bear cub, is so rare along our northern borders that a person would be lucky just to see his tracks.

New York's famous sporting goods store, Abercrombie and Fitch, which for many years advertised polar bear skins for sale, quit the practice in 1966, after protests from conservationists. This, along with the Boone and Crockett Club decision, is good news, though too late for those polar bears whose white fur now hangs on a wall.

3 Thunder on the Plains

From a distance, the two Indians watched the thing they called "the iron snake" move across the wide prairie landscape. At first it was only a dark dot on the horizon. Even far off it made a faint, clacking hum. Smoke and sparks puffed upward from it. Quickly the hum grew to a heavy drone, becoming louder as the mechanical monster chugged nearer. Now it was so close the Indians concealed by the banks of a creek could smell its smoke and feel the ground shake as it thundered forward.

There was fear and resentment on the Indian faces, and helplessness. They watched the train sweep by, its two coaches swaying, men with rifles visible through the open windows. Each year, the railroad tracks stretched deeper into the country of the Cheyennes, Sioux, Arapahoe, and Crow tribes of the Great Plains. The Union Pacific was pressing westward along the Platte River, and the Kansas Pacific's iron monsters were roaring deeper and deeper into Kansas. Southward, still another railroad, the Santa Fe, was striking through the Indian hunting grounds. Wherever the trains went, the white hunters went with them, for this was the land of the giant herds of the American bison— there were so many that they blackened the earth during their seasonal wanderings. For many centuries the Indians had depended upon these bison, or buffalo as they were commonly called, for food, shelter, clothing, and fuel.

Now, in 1867, both the buffalo and the Indians were being driven back by the tide of white men moving westward—hunters, prospectors, settlers, ranchers, and the "iron snake." The buffalo hunters, with their rifles and gunpowder had already killed buffaloes by the thousands, stripping the beasts of their hides and leaving the carcasses for wolves and buzzards to eat. An experienced hunter with a heavy rifle could kill fifty or sixty buffaloes in a day, and with the help of a "skinner" remove the hides to sell. It had been a different thing with the Indians. Once they had not even had horses and had had to pursue the swift buffalo on foot, armed only with spears and arrows, driving the beasts into traps or frightening them into stampeding over cliffs. Even when they had acquired horses from the early Spanish explorers, and could race close to a buffalo, sending arrows through the tough hide, it was a dangerous task and took the efforts of a whole village to bring about a successful hunt.

The Indians at the creek near the Platte River watched silently as the Union Pacific train throbbed past, and then above its clacking wheels they heard another sound, a sound as familiar as the wind whipping the prairie grass, a sound that made their blood stir. It was a low drumming, a rumble that seemed to issue out of the earth itself. There, far off, coming over a rise, was a darkly flowing herd of buffalo. The animals in the lead were scattered and the watchers could see the separate individuals—shaggy-headed bulls with their humped shoulders and beards, the smaller cows, and the calves that had been born in April or June. Now in October the calves had lost their reddish yellow coats and were a sleek brown. The bulls, too, had gained new coats during the summer, their heads now a glossy black where new hair had pushed the old off, curling like dark ferns around the sharp, upward curve of their horns. Noses thrust to the wind, grunting, the bison came onward, so many now that it was no longer possible to see the individual animals but only a mass of bodies rolling like brown surf over the flatly rolling land. The Indians moved, alert to the danger of being trapped in the way of the herd, especially one driving forward as this one was, a dense mass spread out for as many miles in every direction as a man could see. The main body of the herd pressed against the leaders, the animals' heads low, the small, reddish eyes showing through tangles of hair. It was just such herds that the Indians often managed to swerve by waving blankets or burning torches, so that the beasts plunged over the cliffs, unable to stop because of the momentum of the animals crowding from behind. There, wounded or dying, they were comparatively easy to kill. But the Indians by the creek had not come to hunt; even if they had, they were only two against the hundreds of thousands of excited, swarming beasts. Perhaps the buffaloes were in search of water; perhaps they had been alarmed by a prairie fire; perhaps they were merely restless. Whatever the reason for their massive excitement, they kept on snorting across the tableland, slender tails up, hoofs pounding.

It was impossible to count them. Nobody, Indian or white man, knew just how many buffaloes ranged from Mexico up into Canada, and from west of the Missouri River to the Rockies. Estimates went from fifty million to a hundred and twenty-five million. When the white man first came to the shores of America, the buffaloes had roamed as far east as New York, as far west as Oregon. Some were even on the sloping hills of what is now Washington, D.C. Slowly, the buffaloes retreated before the early settlers of the Thirteen Colonies so that by the beginning of the nineteenth century, they had almost disappeared east of the Mississippi. Even so, in the 1860s,

American bison

there seemed still so many on the plains that no matter how many were killed, people believed they would remain forever. "Thick as gnats," the buffalo hunters claimed.

But many of the Indians were worried. The buffaloes were their cattle. If the buffaloes vanished, the Indians

would vanish with them. An old Cheyenne chief, one who had sought to make peace with the white invaders, had predicted in 1846 that the buffaloes would disappear.

There were four great herds, each following regular migration paths over the vast landscape, moving with the seasons, southward in the fall, northward in spring. In cold weather, a hunter could tell the approach of the herds by the spreading clouds of frosty breath that hazed the horizon. In fall and winter, the hides that were prized for robes were at their best, and the meat was fat. Since the majority of white hunters cared nothing about the meat, the carcasses were left to rot. So many bones were scattered over the buffalo range in Kansas, Nebraska, and Wyoming that the land seemed drifted with snow even in summer.

There were a few men, however, who did hunt for buffalo meat. These were men hired by railroad companies to provide the meat for construction gangs. The hundreds of workers slowly but steadily laying rails across the wilderness were far from any city or town where meat supplies were available. And in those days, with no refrigerated freight cars, fresh meat could not be carried across scorching miles of prairie without spoiling. Buffalo meat was the answer for the construction workers and for the troops that camped near the work sites to protect the railroad men from hostile Indians. One of the most famous buffalo hunters who supplied meat to the railroads was a cavalry officer, William C. Cody. In one summer he brought in over four thousand buffaloes, and earned the name of Buffalo Bill.

The thousands of buffaloes killed for meat was only a small fraction of those killed for their hides. If a hide hunter did take any meat, it was the tongue, for this was considered a great delicacy. The tongues brought twenty-five to fifty cents on the market. Properly cured, they were shipped east. Some went to Europe. There is a record of one thousand tongues having been sent to a club in London, the tongues costing a total of five hundred dollars. For such a small amount of money, one thousand American bison were left to rot where they fell.

The Indians had used every part of the buffalo. The rich, dark meat, smoked and cured, provided food in the long months when blizzards swept the land. The hide was used for wigwams, robes, moccasins, and even stretched across frames for boats. The Indians shaped the animal's bones into tools, and used the hollowed-out horns for drinking cups. The droppings, called "buffalo chips" burned well when dry and were often the only source of fuel for the Indians. Without the buffalo the Indians could not have survived, so it is not surprising that they felt a religious gratitude to the giant beast. Before the hunt they held buffalo dances. After the hunt, they would pick out one of the finest skins—sometimes this skin would be that of a rare, white buffalo—and give it to a robe woman who tanned it carefully and ornamented it with beads or quills. When the robe was ready, the warriors took it to a hilltop and spread it out as an offering of thanks to the spirit of the buffalo.

Always there were far more buffaloes than the Indians with their crude weapons could kill, so that the mighty herds continued as they had through centuries. The buffaloes had few animal enemies that could vanquish them. Wolves sometimes managed to kill very young calves, or grown buffaloes that were either sick or crippled. A healthy bull, weighing on an average two thousand pounds, was a match for any predator—except the white men with their increasingly powerful rifles.

Sometimes buffaloes did perish from natural causes. During fierce thunderstorms, lightning might strike a herd, killing as many as a dozen buffaloes pressed together. Tornados occasionally swept the southern plains, sending the beasts into a panic so that they ran blindly and might pile up in gullies or canyons, dying under the weight of their own fellows. Floods, quicksand, and thin ice often meant disaster. Crusted snow, too, was an enemy. Their sharp hoofs broke through the crust so that even a strong bull might be left floundering in a drift, unable to escape a hungry wolf or grizzly bear or Indian. Most troublesome, though not a real danger to the bison, were the gnats and flies that pursued them, especially during the summer when the animals' bodies were naked of protective hair. The clouds of insects swarmed to the buffalo's body, eyes, and nose, biting and stinging until the beast was sometimes driven into a frenzy.

A more serious enemy was drought. Worse still were the fires that swept the prairie grasses. Some of these were caused by lightning, some by Indians and white men. The worst such fire was deliberately set by an army trooper, General Mitchell, in 1865. The year before, Cheyennes had been massacred by white men. They, in turn, attacked the settlers and troopers for over a hundred miles, killing, looting, and burning. So, on a quiet, clear January morning, under orders from Mitchell, men all along the line of the Platte and the South Fork, from the middle of Nebraska to the foothills near Denver, set a row of fires extending for some four hundred and thirty miles.

The separate flames flickered, devouring the tinder provided to give them a good start. The flames licked higher and reached out toward dried whorls of tumbleweed, and seed tops of grass, for although there was ice in the streams there was no snow covering the ground. The fires burned quietly but steadily, as Mitchell had planned, fanning sidewise and creeping forward at the same time. By the time the morning wind began to rise, the fire was a giant crimson chain moving southward where Mitchell hoped to engulf the raiding Indians. Unknown to him, the guilty Indians had already gone north of the Platte River and it was the peaceful bands who remained in the fire's path.

Once the flames were started, nothing could stop them. The smoke reared into the sky, like the clouds of a blizzard. Beneath the smoke was an advancing, hissing wall. All across the four hundred and thirty miles, animals were fleeing—rabbits, pronghorns, coyotes, wolves, and buffaloes. The buffaloes' weak eyesight prevented them from readily seeing the flames, and though their sense of smell was keen, the fire caught many by surprise. Soon one massive herd after another went thundering, bellowing, over the land, stumbling into prairie dog holes, rising again if they were lucky, desperately trying to outrace the searing heat.

Settlers and hunters, too, were threatened by the inferno that drove southward for three days. Domestic cattle, chickens, and horses were devoured by the flames, while their owners took to earthen dugouts. Many of the Indians, long familiar with prairie fires, managed to set backfires around their settlements. These smaller, controlled fires devoured the dry vegetation before the greater flames reached the spot, so that the main fire stopped at the blackened edge, having nothing to feed on.

When the fire finally burned itself out far down in the barren Texas Panhandle, millions of wild creatures were dead, and at least three white hunters—but not one Indian—were lost. Mitchell's revenge had struck chiefly the land and its wild creatures.

Even such a fire was not as destructive as the continuous buffalo hunting that went on with increasing fierceness in the late 1860s. With the railroads boring deeper into the land, more hunters came, thousands of them eager to make a quick fortune out of buffalo hides. Others came just for the sport, shooting the buffaloes from the railroad cars on the Kansas Pacific line. In the fall of 1868, one of the line's trains traveled for a hundred and twenty miles through a browsing herd, often having to stop because the animals refused to get off the tracks in spite of the blasting whistle.

Newspapers and handbills advertised GRAND RAILWAY
EXCURSION and BUFFALO HUNT ON THE PLAINS.
Along the route, business men with an eye to tourist money
built crude hotels, saloons, and dance halls. Magazines
carried romantic stories about Wild Bill Hickok, a mur-
derer of men as well as buffalo, and Buffalo Bill. Buffalo
Bill acted as a personal guide for a Massachusetts Senator
and other eastern visitors, including women. Buffalo Bill,
his long yellow hair flowing, pistols polished, led the party
on a five weeks' tour, thrilling them with stories of Indian
massacres, and showing off his riding skill as he pursued
and killed individual buffaloes.

The Senator's party traveled with tents, wagons, and
even servants. Commercial hunters lived quite differently.
Dirty, unshaven, their clothes stiff with the blood and
tallow of the beasts they skinned, they would stake out a
herd, set up camp, and then settle down to kill as many
buffaloes as they could. Although wounded bulls, or a cow
with a calf, could be dangerous, the work was comparatively
safe for an experienced hunter. If he could work a portion
of a herd into a canyon, where they could not escape,
all he needed to do was to rest his gun barrel on a prop,
and pick off the beasts one by one—keeping a wary eye
out for Indians at the same time. For the Indians, especially
the younger men, were increasingly resentful. They had
been promised by government treaty that the white men
would not take over their High Plains hunting grounds.
The treaty was a forgotten scrap of paper for many in the
government. In fact, it was unofficial policy to destroy
the buffalo as a way of getting rid of the Indian. Certainly
the professional hunter, pulling the trigger of his rifle again
and again, cared nothing about the Indians. What mattered
were the buffaloes dying under his bullets. When he had
finished his kill of anywhere from thirty to sixty (and often

more), he and his assistant, expert in skinning, worked at ripping off the hides. These they pegged down on the ground to dry. Each day, the hunter and the skinner repeated the process. By the time they left camp, the length of their stay depending on weather or the abundance of buffalo, there could be thousands of such hides spread out over the ground. Finally, the two men would pile them into a wagon and head back toward a hide station at the railroad line. There the hides were loaded onto special freight cars and the belching, big-stacked locomotives carried them to eastern cities. Tons and tons of the hides rode over the gleaming rails. During the year 1870, around two million buffaloes were killed for their hides in Nebraska, Kansas, Indian Territory and Texas alone.

Finally, it was not only the Indian who protested such slaughter. Conscientious white men began to push for laws that would stop the carnage. Idaho was the first to outlaw buffalo hunting, in 1864. Wyoming followed in 1871. But in the rest of the states or territories, the protestors were jeered at as "Indian lovers," or meddlers interfering with a free citizen's rights. Those who shouted loudest about their rights were the companies who had begun to organize the hide hunting into a regular business, and freighting firms who added their wagon trains to the scene.

Settlements increased, dotting creeks and rivers. The settlers eyed the lush grasslands, and built up herds of cattle and sheep to graze in the place of the disappearing buffaloes. Very few settlers or hunters, however, in 1870, dared to venture south of the Arkansas River flowing across southern Kansas, a region to which the Indians clung and which the government still recognized as theirs. It was a treasure house of wildlife. Wild turkeys were as thick as the buffaloes. In summer, the prairies were alive with grouse, prairie chickens, curlews, and plovers. An early hide man once shot nearly two hundred of the little prairie plovers in an hour for a group of eastern sportsmen. This area, like the plains region generally, was a thriving grassland community, where each animal, each insect, each root and seed played a vital part. The destruction of any one species affected the well-being of all.

In order to free the grasslands for cattle and sheep, farmers joined the hunters in killing off buffaloes and pronghorns. Wolves, lacking pronghorns or an occasional buffalo to add to their diet of smaller animals turned to killing livestock. So, the farmers' guns were directed at wolves. With the wolves out of the way, rodents increased. Then the rodents were shot and poisoned. Birds fed off poisoned carcasses and died. With the birds gone, the insects multiplied. In the meantime, cattle and sheep overgrazed the grassland so that when rain storms came, there were not enough strong grass roots to hold the soil. Gradually, steadily, much of the once rich grasslands turned into dying land, the topsoil blowing away in hot winds, or turning into gullies from floods. The natural balance and interrelation of the entire grassland community, its "ecology," was upset. Ecology is a study of living things in relation to their environment; the word was coined nearly 100 years ago from two Greek words that mean "the study of the home." Ecology is still a comparatively new science but an increasingly vital one, not only for the preservation of our natural resources and wildlife but also for human beings who also have their "home" in nature.

Once a cycle of destruction of ecological relationships is started, it is almost impossible to stop it. What happened on our Great Plains states a hundred years ago, and in the years following, was brought home to cities far to the east in the 1930s. In Minneapolis, Chicago, Cleveland, Boston, and even as far away as New York, the sky was darkened by rolling clouds of dust . . . soil blown from the plowed fields and over-grazed ranges, which had once been covered by grasses as high as a horse's belly.

Back in 1870, the results of over-grazing and the killing off of wildlife were foreseen by only a very few persons. The slaughter of the buffalo continued, but there were still enough of the animals left to send some two million hides to market in 1871. Even so, the animals were disappearing from their earlier ranges. Around settlements where they had once been abundant, there were only stacks of their bones. In 1874, Montana joined with Idaho and Wyoming in having a law against the hunters, but laws had little effect. Officials who tried to enforce the laws were threatened at gun point, or shown a hangman's noose.

As the original herds north of the Arkansas River thinned, and the buffaloes veered south of the river down into Texas and New Mexico, the hunters followed in spite of the danger from Indians, and in spite of governmental treaty. By 1874, the Indians of the Texas Panhandle had been beaten back, and the hunters carried on with guns aimed at the buffalo there. To the north, one last group of what was called the Republican Herd, still remained, a small herd of the millions that had once roamed the area from southern Kansas up to the Powder River in Wyoming. Thirst-tormented after a long dry season, thousands of buffaloes straggled toward the South Platte River in search of water. They found the river lined with hunters. Thirst was stronger than fear and many desperately lapped up the water in spite of the booming guns. Others turned back, waiting until darkness to return to the river. But darkness was no shield. Men had lighted fires all along the banks for fifty miles. Again the buffaloes that had survived the guns, fled. But thirst drew them back again and again, the next day and night, and still for two days and nights following. After four days and nights, all but a few hundred who escaped northward, were killed. Fifty thousand carcasses lay in and beside the river and in nearby water holes, the stench of their rotting bodies filling the river valley. A Sioux chief, one who had been imprisoned by white men many years before, looked at the remains of this once tremendous central herd with tears running down his cheeks.

The story was repeated to the south, below the Arkansas River, where the Texas herds wandered over country still barely touched by hunters. Now, single hunters killed as many as sixty-three in two hours. One hunter killed over two hundred in one day on less than ten acres of ground. With robes selling for around two and a half dollars each, such hunters were making fortunes, and the wolves were enjoying free feasts. The feasts were not free for long. As the buffalo diminished, hunters turned to taking wolves for their pelts, often by poisoning the buffalo carcasses. Such poisoning killed not only the wolves, but western ravens; the ground for miles was drifted with black-feathered bodies.

The Indians, pushed back on dwindling reservation lands, mourned and could do nothing. There was no longer any question but that the buffaloes would soon vanish completely. Still, the men in Washington did nothing, or were unable to do anything. As the live buffaloes grew scarcer, a new business developed, that of gathering up the millions of bleaching bones to be carted away and developed into fertilizer, bone china, industrial phosphorus, or carbon used by sugar refineries. Some traders made a big business out of the bones, buying them by the ton at a cheap price and then selling them at a profit to the railroads. Farmers, when a year was bad for crops, often managed to survive by collecting the bones on their land.

Although the Republican and Texas herds were, by 1879, scarcely more than a memory, there was still a Northern Herd of about a million, ranging from the lower Yellowstone River up into Canada. The hunters again leaped into their saddles and wagons and headed north. Earlier, these herds had been too far from railroads to make hunting them profitable. But now the Northern Pacific was stretching across North Dakota, westward. By the spring of 1882 there were over five thousand hunters and skinners in the northern range, armed with powerful rifles with telescopic sights. At first the hides shipped back by the railroad numbered around 14,000. Each year the number dropped until in 1884 there were less than 2500, and these were probably carryovers from the year before. In 1885 there were few or no hides at all.

Four years later, Congress put an end to the slaughter, and sent bison hunters out to the Great Plains. These hunters went out not to kill but to search for and save any remaining bison they could find. In the whole area, where by conservative estimate there had been sixty million bulls, cows, and calves, the searchers were able to find only eighty-five survivors in the wild. These animals were given refuge in Yellowstone National Park but even there they were not safe. In 1893, President Grover Cleveland signed a bill making it illegal to kill them in the Park. Elsewhere a few small, privately owned bison herds existed, as well as groups in zoos.

Conservationists, including President Theodore Roosevelt, took further steps to preserve the American bison from extinction. In 1905, the American Bison Society was organized. This Society, with the New York Zoological Society, made an offer to donate fifteen bison to the government if Congress would appropriate sufficient funds to fence an area in the Wichita National Forest and Game Preserve in

Oklahoma. Congress agreed and in October, 1907, fifteen of the finest buffalo from the New York Zoological Park were shipped by rail to Oklahoma.

Seven days later, there was great excitement in the little southwestern town of Cache, Oklahoma, when the train pulled in with its heavily crated cargo of six bulls and nine cows. People from all around flocked to the station to see the shaggy beasts. Among them was the last Comanche chief, Quanah Parker. As the crates were transferred to waiting wagons and hauled the thirteen miles to the Preserve, mounted braves and their squaws followed. The older Indians explained how much the buffaloes had meant to their ancestors in former days.

The small herd prospered and grew. One of the original bulls, Black Dog, lived to achieve the reputation of being the largest living buffalo, weighing an estimated 2800 pounds. Today the Wichita Mountains Wildlife Refuge maintains a herd of between eight hundred and one thousand, thinning out the herd when it becomes too numerous for the size of its range. The biggest of the bulls are not often seen by the public as they are placed in secluded pastures when they become old and dangerous. Even though all the buffalo are behind fences, they are not tame and visitors to the refuge are warned not to go near them as they can and do charge with little warning.

Thanks to the efforts of early conservationists, buffalo herds can still be seen, not only in the Wichita refuge but in Yellowstone Park, and in the National Bison Range in northwestern Montana.

The American bison is not a buffalo, although that is its popular name. The Old World buffalo of Malaya, the Philippines, or India, is a dull, slate-gray animal, nearly hairless, large and bony. The closest relative of the American bison is the bison of Europe, called the wisent. The latter species, also, was nearly exterminated by European hunters, and was only saved by last minute efforts of conservationists in the 1930s.

American bison were not the only animals to diminish and disappear as the western frontier fell back before railroads, river steamers, and covered wagons. On the same range of the great bison lived perhaps five billion other creatures about the size of a small cottontail rabbit, but with much shorter legs and tiny ears. This little creature was the prairie dog, so named for his shrill bark. He and his kind had colonies or "towns" over vast areas of the western plains, single towns extending for ten or twenty

Wisent

miles, and some for 250 miles. These prairie dog towns were marked by low mounds of bare soil and sand which the creatures brought up from underground burrows, burrows that went down steeply from three to fifteen feet. Such holes were dangerous to horseback riders as a horse could easily step into one and stumble or break a leg. Cowboys riding the ranges shot as many of the prairie dogs as they could. Farmers, too, destroyed as many as possible because the small rodents were enemies of their crops, or competed with cattle for grass.

Today, the far flung prairie dog towns have vanished under the works of man, or have been deserted. In March, 1966, all the prairie dogs in the Wichita Mountains Wildlife Refuge in Oklahoma departed overnight. No one knows why they left, or where they went, but such sudden emi-

Black-footed ferret

grations are typical of this animal. Officials in charge of the refuge restocked the colony with thirty-eight new prairie dogs in the hope that they would resettle the empty burrows. The attempt failed. In late October, the refuge manager, Julian A. Howard, and his assistants, tried another approach. In this they were chiefly concerned with trying to discover the reason for the rodents' disappearance, suspecting that it might. be caused by a widespread epidemic. Obtaining six prairie dogs from a neighboring site, they placed them in the center of the depopulated town, in a large wire cage, and fed them. Their idea was that if one of the animals showed any sign of sickness they would rush it to a laboratory to be examined. The prairie dogs stayed healthy and as cold weather approached, the men decided to let the animals go underground. They cut a hole

Prairie dog

in the bottom of the cage and placed it over an abandoned burrow. The prairie dogs immediately cleaned out the burrow and took up residence there—though returning regularly to the cage for a free handout of grain. As of the spring of 1967, at least four of the animals were still present, possibly all.

Practically the only prairie dogs to be seen today are in such refuges. They are among the most entertaining of creatures, playfully chasing each other, but also helping each other build tunnels, and even scratching one another's back. When curious or watchful, they sit up on their hind legs, ears and twitching noses alert. At the first sign of threat—the appearance of a natural enemy such as a hawk, rattlesnake, or coyote—they give their high-pitched, warning bark, tails jerking with every bark, and scurry down into the safety of the burrow. There, they may continue to scold the intruder. Or, if backed into a corner, they will put up a brave fight against even a dog or a coyote.

With the disappearance of the prairie dogs, another interesting animal has grown so scarce that it is included among "endangered species" by the Fish and Wildlife Service. This, the black-footed ferret, is in fact on the edge of extinction. A large member of the weasel family (twenty-two to twenty-four inches long with a six-inch tail), it once ranged the plains in the company of prairie dogs, for the dogs and ground squirrels provided its food. Even though it was once abundant, people seldom saw it because it did most of its hunting at night. Also, although it has a very different shape from that of a prairie dog, when it sits up among the burrows, its black feet folded against its chest, only a very keen eye can detect its presence. The chance

of seeing it at all, under any conditions, is increasingly remote as there are so very few of the ferrets left. Whether
the black-footed ferret will join the ranks of other extinct
species will depend on its being given as much protection
as possible—which must include protection of the remaining
prairie dogs.

4   A Price on Their Heads

A group of men climbed a narrow, icy rock ledge, their breath misting in the winter air. In their lead was a young Connecticut farmer, Israel Putnam, a musket in one hand, and a look of determination on his face. The men with him were neighboring farmers, all looking as grim as he. Ahead of them, higher on the ledge, their dogs barked and cautiously approached a dark opening in the smooth rocks about two feet square. There was no sound from within the deep den but each man in the group could visualize the wolf that the bloodhounds had chased there, a wolf that had been killing livestock in the area for several years. Her tracks were clearly visible in the light snow, showing the lack of toes on one crippled foot. The animal had lost the toes in a steel trap, but that was the closest she had come to being captured. Handicapped for hunting wild game such as deer, she had turned to destroying sheep and other farm animals to sustain herself and litters of cubs. Now at last she was cornered. The men had come equipped with straw and sulphur to try to smoke her out of her hiding place. They set fire to bundles of straw, sprinkled them with sulphur which released poisonous fumes, and tossed the burning material as deeply as possible into the downward slanting entrance of the den. The fumes filled the cavern but there was no sign of the renegade wolf.

For hours, Putnam and the men tried every way they knew to flush out the wolf, without success. Night came but Putnam refused to give up. Ever since he had started farming on a large tract of land at Pomfret in 1739, this particular wolf had killed his sheep and goats and managed to escape in spite of all that anyone could do. Putnam urged his dog to go into the opening, which slanted downward for ten feet and ended in blackness, but the dog whimpered and balked. Putnam then ordered his Negro slave to go in, but the Negro, too, drew back. Angry, fearful that the wolf might escape through some invisible opening in the rocks, Putnam declared that he himself would go in. His companions protested such a dangerous venture. Putnam ignored their protests and ordered them to bring him some birch bark for a torch. Next he pulled off his coat and waistcoat, and had a long rope fastened around his legs so that at a signal his neighbors could drag him back out of the cavern. He lighted the birch bark, then holding it in one hand, he crawled headfirst into the aperture.

The narrow, sloping tunnel was no wider in any spot than three feet, the roof pressing down. Putnam slid and scraped downward for ten feet and found that the tunnel became horizontal. Ahead of his flickering torch there was only darkness. Putnam crawled onward, to find the tunnel sloping upward. Slowly, climbing on his hands and knees, he went on, the torch's wavering light revealing only more rocks, more shadows—and then, suddenly, the gleam of eyes. There was the wolf crouched at the very end of the cavern, teeth bared, growling. Triumphant at finding the animal there with no means of escape, Putnam kicked the rope as a signal for the other men to pull him out. The men outside had heard the wolf's growl; thinking that

Putnam had been attacked, they pulled him out of the cave so swiftly that his shirt was ripped up over his head and when he reached the ledge he was bruised and bleeding. Scarcely taking time to look at his scratches, Putnam loaded his musket with nine buckshot, took a fresh birch torch, and descended a second time. Cautiously, he again approached the wolf. The animal crouched, at bay, ready to spring. Putnam fired. The roar pounded against his ear drums, and the musket smoke choked him. At his signal, his helpers drew him out of the cave. After a moment's rest, while he waited for the smoke to clear, he went once more into the wolf's den. The wolf was dead. This time, when Putnam's friends hauled on the rope, they dragged both Putnam and the wolf out, with a cheer.

Long before Putnam's time, the early colonists on the eastern seaboard had waged war on wolves. The wolf was the first animal in the New World to have a price put on its head. In 1630, the Massachusetts Bay Colony established a bounty system, offering one penny for every wolf shot. Even for that small a reward, it is said that some men supported themselves by shooting wolves, so they must have managed to shoot a great many.

In those days, wolves were almost everywhere, spreading across the North American continent from east to west, and from northern Mexico up into the Arctic. The wolves fell into two main groups. There was the gray wolf, also called the timber wolf, a large wolf of the plains and the north. A smaller wolf, the red wolf, or Texas wolf, tended to roam the south. The ranges of the two overlapped, frequently. Before the coming of the white man, the wolves hunted freely, amply supplied with food ranging from small rodents to bison. Swift, cunning, and in the case of the gray wolf, powerful, these creatures of the dog family were able to hold their own against almost all enemies.

In this country, as well as in Europe, the wolf has played an important part in legends. Unfortunately for the wolf's reputation, many of these stories depict him as a fierce, bloodthirsty creature eager to prey on human beings. "Werewolves" were supposed to be vicious wolves in human disguise. Wolves, also, were said to be able to disguise themselves as witches, or to play cruel tricks, as in the story of Red Riding Hood. Even in present-day cartoons, the wolf is invariably the villain. Probably no animal has been so persecuted and unfairly represented as the wolf. Parkman shared the common attitude when, as in the quotation in the preface to this book, he referred to wolves as "squalid" and "ruffian-like." In contrast, many other authors who have seen wolves in the wild have commented on their handsomeness, grace, and dignity. On the prowl, a wolf pack uses close teamwork. Before a hunt, the animals congregate, touch noses, and wag their tails in what seems to be a form of communication. Each animal has a certain position in the pack, the pack often being led by a top male and a top female who do not necessarily mate with each other. At least one member of a wolf family is always on guard to warn of danger. And it can happen that if danger does occur, wolves outside the immediate family group may help out, as in a case reported where four wolves took on four grizzlies which threatened young pups. Rangers watched the battle through binoculars until the bears, badly slashed, left. As for wild wolves made captive, Dr. Jerome H. Woolpy of the University of Chicago found that he could make friends of adult wolves by sitting quietly in their cages for ten minutes every day over a period of six months. In time, the wolves greeted him like friendly, excited dogs.

Dr. Adolph Murie, in his book, *A Naturalist in Alaska*, tells of his experience in Mount McKinley National Park where he lived in close contact with wolves. He followed the tracks of wolves after a late May snowfall. When he came close to a wolf den he startled a male wolf that ran off and then with a backward glance, howled and barked at him. A female within the den put her head out, withdrew, then ran out, leaving a litter of pups behind. Murie crawled in and removed three of the pups, but the wolves, fearing man far more than grizzlies, did nothing more than bark at him although he took one of the pups away. The experience of other scientists has been similar. Dr. Douglas H. Pimlott, of the University of Toronto, writing of his own experiences studying wolves, states, "Even though we have worked and traveled unarmed in wolf country, often living close to them, we have never been threatened in any serious way."

Around the time that Columbus sailed toward America, the wolf was already nearly extinct in England. And as soon as the first colonial settlers of the United States arrived with their horses, cattle, sheep, and swine, the war against wolves began in the New World. After about a hundred years, the wolf was practically extinct throughout New England and eastern Canada. Pushed backward by civilization, the wolves retreated westward and northward. Guns and traps were not the only reason they did so. The cutting down of forests deprived the wolves of their ancient hunting grounds, and the killing of wild game took away their natural food supply. This included not only mammals but almost everything edible, from wild fruits, grasshoppers, snails, fish, birds, or ants. Wolves, like bears and coyotes, are omnivorous.

So numerous were the wolves in the western frontier days that a kind of counting game became popular with travelers of that time. Charles Hoffman, one of the early travelers, published a book of his travels in the West in

Gray wolf

1835. He described how, as he and a companion rode across the prairie, they played this game.

"I was contented to wrap myself as closely as possible in my buffalo robe, and join him in a game of prairie loo . . . the game consists merely in betting upon the number of wild animals seen by either party toward the side of the vehicle on which he is riding, a wolf or deer counting ten, a grouse one. The game is a hundred; and you may judge of the abundance of these animals from our getting through several games before dinner . . . my companion looing me with eleven wolves. Some of these fellows would stand looking at us within half gunshot, as we rode by them."

If one tried to play such a game while riding in an

automobile today, the chances of seeing even one wolf is so unlikely that nobody would even suggest the game.

The greatest toll of wolves came at the time the bison were being slaughtered in vast numbers. Many of the big gray wolves that had followed the bison found refuge in the mountain wildernesses of the north and the northwest. Those who remained on the plains ended in farmers' traps, or died of poison placed in the carcasses of dead bison or other animals. Cowboys, passing a dead bison, or steer, stopped to hide a deadly strychnine tablet in the flesh. This poison killed wolves, but it killed many other animals such as kit foxes, as well. Another method of wolf control was to set fire to woods, especially along timbered water courses. Packs of wolf-hunting dogs were trained, also, with results satisfactory to the stockmen. Professional "wolfers" hired out to ranchmen and made a good living at five dollars a skin.

A few of the strongest and craftiest of the wolves managed to outwit all attempts to eliminate them. One of the most famous was a lone wolf called "Custer" who roamed along the border between Wyoming and South Dakota. For ten years this wily wolf avoided bullets and traps, preying on cattle. Even when a five-hundred-dollar bounty was placed on him, he continued to outwit the hunters. Finally, the ranchers appealed to the Biological Survey. A well-known hunter, H. P. Williams, set out to track Old Custer down. After six months, Williams succeeded.

Considering how wolves have been harried and hounded, it is remarkable that any are left. The gray wolf of the plains is extinct, but a few of his brothers—the timber wolf —have managed to survive in certain sections of the continent: western Canada, Alaska, Isle Royale National Park in Michigan, and in remote forests of Michigan and Wisconsin. The Minnesota wolves which range the regions near that state's Superior National Forest are now protected but as late as 1966 there were county bounties of thirty-five dollars per wolf. Alaska still pays a fifty-dollar bounty for every wolf killed, whether by trap or shooting.

By 1963, the wolves in upper Michigan and Wisconsin were down to perhaps a couple of dozen; their survival is debatable. The wolves on Isle Royale arrived there around 1950, crossing the ice from Ontario. They were in luck for the island was a national park well-supplied with wild moose—too many moose, in fact, for the island's vegetation to support. With the coming of the wolves, the moose population was reduced so that fewer moose were in danger of slow death by starvation or disease. A scientific ten year study was undertaken in 1958, by Purdue University, with the support of the National Park Service, the National Science Foundation, and the Wildlife Management Institute, to learn more about the relationships between predators and their prey. In 1963, researchers found that the wolf population on the island had stayed stable for three years, numbering only around twenty-two individuals, male and female. Biologists are hopeful that both moose and the timber wolf will survive there, striking a natural balance, so that the deep howl of the wolf will not disappear forever from the land.

This increasingly rare sound has been described as less a howl than "singing." Wildlife researchers report that "howl-alongs" have a musical variety. At intervals there are duets, "melodious arias," "rambling cadenzas," or a "mass chorale." In the Algonquin Provincial Park of Ontario there is an organized evening program called a "wolf howl." Cars of tourists follow a park naturalist who stops at certain spots to play an amplified recording of wolves' voices, to which packs of wolves respond.

The chief refuge in the United States for the gray wolf is

Alaska's Mount McKinley National Park, an area of three thousand square miles of rolling tundra and glacier-fed rivers, where the gray wolf is protected from all hunters— but bounty hunters in airplanes are a threat even here. This is one of the last places that animal lovers can see this intelligent, gray-to-black, creature in the wild. Weighing from eighty to one hundred fifty pounds, thirty inches high at the shoulder, the gray wolf is powerful and fleet and adept at chasing and bringing down the caribou, the northern deer that migrate through parts of the Park.

Rare though the gray wolf is, the Texas, or red wolf, is even rarer and may vanish completely. Unlike the northern wolf, it has not been able to flee into Alaskan or Canadian wilderness areas. In 1932 there were still a few small packs in western Mississippi, but the last known red wolf there was taken in 1946. Nor has one been positively identified in Missouri since around 1950. Small populations still exist along the Texas coast and possibly in one or two isolated areas of Louisiana. Whether there are any left in Arkansas is not known. These reddish, beautifully-marked wolves still fall prey to poisons put out under predator control programs in which federal agents take part, because of appeals from sheepmen and ranchers.

Wolves are social animals and they tend to travel in packs, especially when hunting. Both the male and the female take care of the pups and are devoted parents. The average litter is between four to six pups born in a den or cave. The father wolf brings food home to the mother while she is nursing the young. Wolves mate for life and there have been many stories about the strong bond between such mated pairs.

In spite of many stories to the contrary, wolves of North America have rarely, if ever, attacked human beings without provocation. And though it is true that wolves fre-

Red wolf

quently killed livestock, such killings were usually by "renegade" killers such as the one Israel Putnam shot. Many
persons have tamed wolves and found them docile and
affectionate. One of these men is Dr. Benson Ginsburg,
professor of biology at the University of Chicago. In a
newspaper article in 1962, he told about three wolves he
had bottle-fed from puppyhood. "The more you live with
wolves," he wrote, "the more you realize that dogs are only

incomplete wolves. Wolves are highly social, friendly, and intelligent—more so than dogs. They're so smart they can unlatch their own cages." And so tame that his nine-year-old daughter played with them.

We cannot all have a pet wolf and probably would not want one. Fortunately, we can see wolves in zoos. When they are well-treated, they settle down and bear their pups as they would in the wilds, the mother taking lavish care of her offspring. There are also a few of the rare red wolves in zoos, and some of these were born in captivity, so there is a good chance that the species will continue. However, all true animal lovers hope that wild, free wolves will never disappear from our world.

The same hope extends to another member of the dog family, that musical, sly, and swift creature called the coyote. Considerably smaller than the gray wolf, weighing up to fifty pounds, the coyote formerly was heavily concentrated in the western half of the United States. The first white men who saw him gave him various names. Common to the prairies, he was called the "prairie wolf" by some, a "burrowing dog" by others. Eventually, the Spanish-derived name, coyote, stuck to him.

Cowboy songs are full of references to the coyote's habit of "singing," a sound that was once characteristic of prairie nights and dawns. Hearing the distant yipping of coyotes is an enchanting experience. It seems especially precious not only for the touch of an almost forgotten wildness it brings to the landscape, but because the coyote is another creature that has been hunted mercilessly by raisers of live-stock or domestic fowl. Both private and government "coyote getters" have, for years, tried to exterminate the coyote. Yet the coyote, like the wolf, has an important role in nature and even in ranching or farming. This is well-illustrated by a story told by J. Frank Dobie in his book,

The Voice of the Coyote. He describes how an eager young hunter came to a Texas rancher, George West, and asked if he might hunt deer on the man's ranch. No, Mr. West said; hunters shooting at deer would frighten his steers and the steers would run so hard they would lose all their fat. Well then, the young man asked, could he hunt coyotes? Mr. West shook his head. The coyotes were needed to keep the jack rabbits down; otherwise the jack rabbits would multiply so fast they would eat up all the grass. In that case, the hunter said eagerly, he would just shoot jack rabbits. Sorry, said Mr. West, but the jack rabbits were needed to feed the coyotes.

Not all ranchers appreciate or understand the balance of nature so well, nor seem concerned that when poison is planted in bait for the coyote, many other creatures are endangered as well. Like the wolf, the coyote eats anything and everything including dead animals, carrion—and is, unfortunately for his survival, fond of sheep. However, a pair of eminent biologists who studied the coyote's food habits, concluded that eighty per cent of his food consisted of rabbits, mice, insects, wild birds and plants. Unlike wolves, who do their hunting in packs, the coyotes most often hunt singly although they do delight in coming together, especially at night, to sit on their haunches, sharp noses turned up toward the sky, while they serenade the stars or moon. Hundreds of stories and fables emphasize the coyote's intelligence, and these are corroborated by fact. The coyote is one of the few animals who has learned to profit from automobiles. At night and in early morning, he patrols the highways for the dead rabbits, skunks, birds and other creatures that have been struck by cars. Only occasionally does *Senor Coyote* get hit. He usually looks both ways before dashing across a highway. A story is told about one coyote who was caught in a trap. This trap had a chain on it with a three-pronged grappling hook, at the end. With one foot caught in the trap, the coyote tried to escape, dragging the trap with him. The trailing hook kept catching in small bushes and jerking the coyote back. The hunter, following the coyote, saw the animal finally pick the hook up in its mouth and carry it.

Thanks to his intelligence and his adaptability, the coyote survives and has extended his range eastward, northward, southward and, in Oregon, westward. Before the Klondike gold rush in 1898, there were no coyotes in Alaska, as there are now. And some occur in the eastern states, as they did not formerly. Even so, they have been largely exterminated over the plains and prairies where they were originally so abundant, and have no legal protection. With a thirty-dollar bounty paid for each coyote killed in Alaska, who can tell how long the coyote's voice will continue to be heard even there?

The voice of another member of the dog family will not be heard again. That is the Great Plains species of fox known as the swift fox. This dainty member of the kit fox group, which seldom measured more than a yard long including its long bushy tail, was exterminated in the wake of the bison and the plains wolf. The swift fox fed chiefly on desert rodents, rabbits, insects, lizards, and birds. The kit foxes of the Southwest are becoming increasingly rare, their pelts joining those of the coyote pelts nailed to fence posts. Yet all admirers of animals who have seen the wild kit fox, the pigmy of the fox species, have been struck by its grace and beauty.

For years, defenders of wildlife have fought against what they consider extreme predator-control programs. Predators are animals that prey on other animals, and include wolves, coyotes, foxes, badgers, wolverines, lynxes, bobcats, and mountain lions. If these animals preyed only on each other,

Swift fox

ranchers, farmers, and sportsmen would not be concerned. But because certain of them do attack domestic animals and birds, or game such as pheasant and deer, there has been a continual attempt to eliminate them, starting back in the 1600s with the wolf bounties. Since that time, more than a hundred species of animals have appeared on North American bounty lists. Bounties are cash payments to the hunter or trapper who brings in evidence that he has killed a predator, and the payments are made mostly from state and county funds.

As of March, 1931, another type of program, administered by the Branch of Predator and Rodent Control of the Fish and Wildlife Service, took over the major role in destroying predators and "pests." In 1966 money spent by

Wolverine

local and Federal agencies in the United States for predator control, in all its phases, amounted to nearly seven million dollars, local expenditures being about twice that of the Federal government.

The result of such campaigns of destruction has been that even individuals with an interest in farming or trapping, appeared before a House of Representatives investigating committee in Washington, D.C., March 1966, to protest the general effects of the program. Leonard Hall, a Missouri livestock farmer who is also a conservationist, pointed out that he had traveled throughout the Southwest and found vast areas of rangeland so terribly over-grazed that they would no longer support either cattle or sheep. "Yet, in these very areas, the fences are weighted down with the carcasses of harmless hawks, kit foxes, bobcats, eagles and coyotes—the fruit of the ceaseless campaign carried on by ranchers and Federal agents with gun, poison and trap . . . Some of these overgrazed areas subjected to predator control programs even include national parks and monuments."

Another spokesman, Paul Maxwell of Colorado, representing the National Trappers' Association, spoke out for the protection of such animals as the coyote and bobcat, and especially against indiscriminate poisoning. "I feel in our expanding population we will always have sheep. That is a settled fact. But our wildlife is really priceless. You can't put a dollar and cents valuation on it. When it's gone, it will never be replaced. It's gone forever."

As a result of such investigations and scientific study, the Federal predator-control program was revised in the spring of 1967 with an eye to more caution and selectivity in destroying wildlife pests, with particular regard to ecology and rare or endangered species.

One of the endangered animals that has long been included on the predator list, and which may vanish completely outside of zoos, is the mountain lion, sometimes called panther, puma, or cougar.

"Long shadows stretched across the woodland trail as Buckskin Bill walked toward his homestead. Suddenly, close by, there was a high-pitched scream. Bill wheeled. There, on an overhanging tree branch, was a panther, its brute body crouched to spring, its jaws crimson from a recent feast. Bill raised his rifle even as the panther exploded into furious action, fangs flashing, claws hissing through the air, ready to rip human flesh. The trusty rifle split the forest silence and the tawny, bloodthirsty killer landed with a final snarl at the homesteader's feet."

This was the way the mountain lion was pictured in the cheap novels of years ago. The authors of such fiction knew nothing about the mountain lion, but the animal was a

handy villain and so they used him to give their readers
a thrill. The majority of persons who read such stories
and went out west, imagined they saw mountain lions
behind every bush. If one of their steers or sheep was
killed, they were certain a mountain lion had done it. If a
child was terrified by some movement behind a tree, the
child often went crying home to say that a mountain lion
had waylaid it.

The truth is that the mountain lion fears and avoids man,
and that many a pioneer discovered that children could
play unwatched in mountain lion country without any danger. In the few recorded cases where a lion has attacked
human beings, the animal was starving, confused, or react-
ing in self-defense. Where deer or elk are plentiful, the
lion will usually hunt these. It is only when such game has
been killed off by the hunter's gun that a hungry lion may
turn to domestic animals. Unlike wolves and coyotes, the
lion does not capture its prey by running it down. It
specializes in stealth, moving noiselessly on its heavily
padded feet, keeping out of sight, then taking its quarry by
surprise. When excited, it switches its tail like a domestic
cat watching a mouse. Both the mountain lion and the
house tabby belong to the same family, as do the lynx,
bobcat, cheetah, and the beautifully spotted jaguar which
is extremely rare and found in the United States only on
the southern borders of Arizona and New Mexico.

One of the mountain lion's chief traits is playfulness.
Indians tell stories of how the big cat, as long as he does
not feel threatened, will follow the tracks of a man in the
snow, carefully putting each paw exactly inside the im-
pression of the man's footprints as if playing a game. Sleeping campers have sometimes wakened to find a lion snuffing
around them in curiosity and making cooing sounds like a
pigeon, before bounding off into the darkness.

In colonial days, mountain lions were relatively common throughout the country, and had the widest range of any large mammal in the New World. But by the time of the Revolutionary War the eastern mountain lion was exterminated. Today, the animals have only a few strongholds left, and even those are diminishing. The last major refuge

of mountain lions in the United States is in Glacier National Park in western Montana.

Because mountain lions are so wary, it is very difficult to take an accurate count of their numbers. Six western states were believed, in 1966, to have five hundred or more cougars each: Arizona, California, Idaho, New Mexico, Utah and Washington. Possibly Nevada and Montana had as many, with anywhere from two hundred to three hundred in Colorado, Oregon, and Texas. In the east and south, only Florida sustained a couple of hundred, more or less. Generally, in the west, the mountain lions cling to the higher mountain areas.

Where these lions have disappeared, deer populations increase so that they do permanent damage to the top soil and forest, while thousands of the deer die from starvation (50,000 in the Michigan woods in 1950–51), or in their hunger roam down to orchards and gardens to nibble prize fruits and flowers. Worse, the hungry deer frequently wander onto highways and cause serious accidents to motorists. Although licensed hunters are permitted to shoot deer at certain seasons of the year, they are normally restricted to shooting prime bucks. All too often, the diseased or weak animals are left and so the deer herd becomes scrawny, undersized, or otherwise defective. Many residents in northern California are plagued by the depredations of starving deer. A mountain lion in such areas should be a welcome sight. Instead, if by some chance one is seen —it usually turns out to be a yellow dog or large, yellow house cat—people rush for their guns, eager to pursue and kill the "bloodthirsty" intruder.

The basically shy, always wary mountain lion, is one of the most beautiful of our wild creatures. Even in a zoo, he is an animal of impressive grace and quiet majesty. His color varies from a light tan to a tawny brown which, in

sunlight, becomes a shining gold. His head is dispro-
portionately small, his body and tail long, his length being
from six to eight feet. An average male may weigh 165
pounds. The female is smaller, weighing up to one hundred
pounds. Furry kittens spotted with blackish brown are
born in late winter or early spring, and stay with the
mother for two years, though they usually start foraging
for themselves when they are around a year old. If a mother
lion is killed, the kits will linger about the spot for several
days and repeatedly return to the place where she died. Or,
if a kit is lost, the mother will hunt for it anxiously.

Only a few years ago, the state of California paid a six-
hundred-dollar bounty on the mountain lion and the county
in which the lion was killed paid another seventy-five
dollars. Even though the lions were not easy to find, some
hunters managed to make a business out of killing them.
In 1963, California called a four-year halt on the mountain
lion bounty. In May, 1967, the moratorium was made
permanent.

Another California mammal was granted protection at
the same time. The ringtail cat, a swift and graceful animal
that was once a pet of gold miners, was removed from
bounty payments. The two pound ringtail is an excellent
mouser and early miners encouraged it to stay around
their dwellings to keep down the rodent population. The
animal became known as a "miner's cat," also "coon cat"
because of the dark bands that go halfway around its long
tail. Rapidly vanishing, this fox-faced animal is now protected in California, like the mountain lion, the sea otter,
the fur seal, and mountain sheep.

The fate of all these creatures rests in man's hands—
those of the individuals who make our laws, and those
with rifles who rush out to kill whatever wild thing moves
through the shadows of mountain, forest, or plain.

5　Wild Hoofs

It was Christmas Day, 1966, with late morning sunlight shining over the ochre, lavender-shadowed mountains enclosing the Death Valley National Monument in California. In front of the Monument's glass-walled natural history museum, a Federal ranger stood talking to a group of visitors about the geology, history, flora and fauna of the famous valley which is 280 feet below sea level. On each side of the valley, the Panamints and the Funeral Ranges, their peaks touched with new snow, stretched in wrinkled folds. Though, in summer, Death Valley is one of the hottest areas on earth, the visitors shivered in the brisk wind and moved eagerly after the ranger as he led them toward the shelter of some lacy trees growing alongside a nearby creek. The trees grew thickly beside the stream, their delicate leaves waving in the wind. Except for these, and a plantation of date palms, the landscape was bare of anything except desert shrubs.

Someone commented on the beauty of the lacy trees. The ranger nodded but said, "These trees are one of our serious problems here."

There was general bewilderment among the visitors for it was difficult to imagine how such a lovely tree in so treeless an area could ever be a problem.

"This tree is a tamarisk, an import from Asia," the ranger went on, "and the people who planted it thought they were doing Death Valley a favor. Unfortunately, the tamarisk is a tremendous consumer of water. It seeds itself and grows rapidly wherever water is available." He waved his hands toward the mountains. "Wherever there are springs, the tamarisk moves in. But the springs are desperately needed by the various forms of wildlife we have here, especially the bighorn sheep. The trees suck up the water that our bighorns need, and once established the tamarisk is almost impossible to get rid of." As he looked toward the cliffs and parapets of the distant peaks there was no doubt, by his expression, that he considered the bighorn sheep more vaulable by far than the green loveliness, shelter, or shade of the tamarisk.

Another threat to the bighorns that the ranger did not mention, although he was unquestionably aware of it as are all conservation personnel in desert bighorn country, is that of the wild burro. There are a number of cases in our history where tame animals have reverted to the wild. Such animals are called feral animals. Dogs, cats, and horses have become feral animals, usually because they are left to shift by themselves. Herds of wild mustangs have been the basis for exciting stories and legends. Before the Civil War there was an estimated several million head of wild horses running free. After World War II, airplanes were used to round up the wild horses which were then killed and the meat used for canned dog food. By the late 1950s there were only a few wild bands left. In 1959, Congress prohibited rounding up wild horses or burros on Federal lands.

Also a part of western frontier literature are the famous longhorns of Texas, Arizona, and New Mexico, descendants of cattle brought in by the early Spanish explorers, which then strayed and reverted to the wild. A representative herd was given refuge in 1927 in the Wichita Mountains Wildlife Refuge in Oklahoma and is there today.

The wild burro continues to occur in many western states, but especially in California, Arizona, Nevada, and New Mexico. Mostly these burros are in widely-scattered bands in barren regions where food and water are scarce. So, even though they may not be present in great numbers, there are still enough to compete with other desert animals for what the arid land has to offer. Although they are furtive, they have been known to fight with cattle over watering troughs, or chase off bighorn ewes and lambs from natural water holes. In Death Valley, in 1935, the National Park Service began a long term study of the relationship between the wild, shaggy burros and the desert bighorn. They found that wherever burros increased, the bighorn population dwindled.

There are not many of the Nelson bighorn sheep in Death Valley, perhaps one hundred or so, but then there are not a great many of the bighorns left anywhere compared to what there were in earlier days. The Rocky Mountain bighorn and the other sub-species of bighorn, such as the Nelson bighorn, once ranged through the Rocky Mountains from southern Alberta and British Columbia south to northern Mexico and the southernmost tip of Lower California. The Rocky Mountain sub-species has been driven into the remote wilderness areas of its range. The more eastern race, the Bad Lands bighorn of North Dakota, western South Dakota, western Nebraska, and eastern Montana and Wyoming has been exterminated. The northernmost of the bighorns is the white Dall sheep of Alaska, which is still fairly abundant where wilderness remains untouched. But each day, the wilderness retreats before the advance of civilization.

Because bighorns keep to high mountain peaks, few people have a chance to see them. Bighorn sheep weigh from 125 (females) to 320 pounds (males), and are gray-brown with creamy white rumps. They are nimble acrobats on the mountain ledges, leaping over chasms, clattering down steep rock walls with ease. Mornings they usually spend feeding on bushes and plants. At night they seek out familiar resting places that are sheltered by overhanging rock where they are protected from rain and snow and from hunters. Constantly alert, the big rams often seek out a pinnacle where they stand watch, scanning the land below for danger.

At breeding time the rams hold their annual mating battles. In these the rivals crash into each other head on, their massive, curled horns bearing the shock. The horns of the older males sometimes curl backward to make a

Bighorn sheep

complete circle. Once in a great while the battles are so
fierce that a ram is killed by his opponent. The horns are
permanent and are not shed from season to season as with
deer. Unhappily for this mountain sheep, the massive
horns are among the favorite trophies of hunters, even
though the hunter must climb rugged mountainsides far
above timberline to get them. Though the bighorn is a
better climber than his human foe, and is quick to spot
danger, he is by no means safe. Nor are protective laws any
guarantee of safety. Poachers, determined to have a bighorn's head stuffed and mounted on a den wall, wait at
water holes, guns ready. Sometimes such hunters remain by
the water holes, hidden by blinds, for several days. When
the big sheep comes within range, their guns blast away.
After the hunters have departed, only headless carcasses
remain.

Not all are so indifferent to the survival of these increasingly rare, hoofed mountain climbers. In Arizona
recently the Arizona Game and Fish Department, the Forest
Service, the U. S. Marines, the Air Force and the Army all
worked together to provide a water tank for thirsty desert
bighorns in the Santa Catalina Mountains outside Tucson.
Although there is a sufficiency of water in the Catalinas
at certain times of the year, the mountains tend to be dry
just at the time that growing lambs, born in the spring, are
most in need of it. The wildlife manager of Arizona's Game
and Fish Department, Bob Hernbrode, decided that fewer
lambs would die if a reliable summer source of water could
be provided by means of a tank which would collect
seepage from the rocks in a remote canyon where the bighorns came to drink. He went to work to put his plan in
action.

From March until July, residents in and near Tucson
saw some unusual activity going on. First, an Air Force

helicopter went whirring over the chosen site to scout the area, and lowered Hernbrode, Capt. Tom Newkirk of the Marines, and a reporter, Tom Foust, to inspect the high, rugged spot. Hernbrode calculated that around 100,000 gallons of water a year seeped out of the rocks there and that with a small dike, a water pipe, and a tank to hold the water, a storage basin could be built. The tank was to be provided by the U. S. Forest Service.

The next weekend, ten Marines trudged upward over the cactus-studded slopes, each carrying thirty pounds of cement on his back, together with tools, for building the dike. At the canyon site, the men mixed the cement with sand scraped from the rocks, and water collected in cans. It was dark before the men finished, but when they left, the dike was built.

Lowering a heavy, dangling water tank from a helicopter was less simple. First, the Army officials at Fort Huachuca, about sixty miles from Tucson, donated a "chopper" to carry the 750-pound tank. The tank swung so badly that the pilot had to drop it to save the ship, and the tank was badly dented. Next, the Forest Service provided a helicopter which it seemed might do the job. Halfway to the canyon site, the harness supporting the tank broke and the tank went plummeting to earth and was smashed beyond repair. Finally, a cooperative effort between a truck and a helicopter succeeded. The truck, carrying a new tank, chugged as far as it could to the mouth of Pima Canyon. There, a helicopter picked the tank up and flew it safely to the site. With a few final touches, "Operation Bighorn" was done, and all those who worked on it hoped that it would mean an increase in the bighorn population.

In spite of such efforts, civilization remains the greatest threat to the bighorns. They are especially vulnerable to the diseases of domestic animals. When they come down to graze at lower altitudes they often find sheep grazing in the same area, and if the sheep are diseased the germs spread to the bighorns. Also, the sheep devour the same plants the bighorns depend on for food.

Their only real sanctuaries are the national game reserves, but even there they are not completely secure. Persistently, gunners keep pressing to have parts or all of present reserves opened to shooting. Or, if refuges are near military proving grounds, as in the Kofa Game Range in southwestern Arizona, there are pressures from the military to use the land for gunnery practice. Even the Kenai National Moose Range in Alaska where many wild animals are protected, including the handsome white Dall bighorn, is not completely wilderness. Part of it is being used for agriculture and settlement.

This refuge was established in 1941 to give protection to the big Kenai moose, the largest of the North American deer tribe. In order to prevent these moose from increasing beyond the natural food supply, there are regular open seasons for public hunting. The same problem of over-population exists in other refuges or wilderness lands where natural predators such as the wolf or mountain lion have been removed. These animals would normally keep moose, deer, and elk populations within bounds. The native, Kenai Peninsula wolf, however, was wiped out a few decades ago. So, a situation has developed where federal and state game management officials find themselves obliged to go in and kill "rare" wildlife.

An example of this is what happened to the Michigan elk. Next to the 1000-pound moose, the elk—also known by its Indian name, wapiti—is the largest American deer. Elk migrate more than other deer. Once, they roamed widely across the United States but are now found mainly along the Coast Ranges from northern California up through

Vancouver, and in the Rockies from Idaho into New Mexico. Only the males have antlers. Like the bighorns, the bucks fight for mates, antlers crashing together and sometimes locking so that neither animal can get free.

Elk were once abundant in Michigan but were wiped out by hunters, settlers, and loggers. In 1919, it was decided to try to restore the animals and so eight adult elk were collected from parks and refuges and released in one county in the state's Sturgeon River country. The elk thrived and became an attraction to tourists. By 1964, the elk had multiplied to a herd of 3500 and had spread over four counties. Soon there were signs of over-grazing, and of elk dying of starvation. The Michigan Department of Conservation decided it had to do something, but it was not easy to persuade anti-hunting groups that hunters should be permitted to kill off any of the animals. Nevertheless, hunting was sanctioned. In the fall of 1964, the hunters drew lots for a chance at the big game, paying $25 each, and 300 of them went into the woods for the hunt. They killed 269 elk and, in the following year, 183. Similar measures have been taken in other states where certain forms of protected wildlife exceed the ability of the range to provide food.

There are only two remaining herds of America's (and the world's) smallest elk, the tule elk. Unique to California, the tule elk are shorter legged than other elk, lighter in color, and the largest weigh little more than seven hundred pounds. These elk once numbered many thousands and ranged widely through the valleys of California west of the Sierra Nevada. Driven to seek shelter from hunters, especially during and after California's Gold Rush period, a last remnant of the original herds left the grassy valleys that had long been their home and in 1873 sought refuge among marshes where a Western bulrush called tule

grows. These few survivors happened to end up on a Kern County ranch where the owners gave them protection. Government protection followed. By 1914 this protected herd numbered over 400.

Attempts were made to transplant the animals to other favorable locations but these were generally unsuccessful. In 1932, the State Park Commission purchased nearly 1000 acres of land north of Tupman and placed 75 tule elk within an enclosure there but the animals did not thrive under such artificial conditions. The elk were still without a wild home until 1933 when private individuals, in co-operation with local agencies, managed to arrange for 27 elk to be released in California's Owens Valley. In spite of the protective mountain walls about the little valley, the elk were by no means safe from the guns or the dogs of ranchers, especially those with alfalfa fields in the area since the elk did graze the alfalfa when their natural browse was low. Nevertheless, the elk thrived and increased and, under pressure from cattlemen and sportsmen, the State Fish and Game Department in 1943 authorized a hunt that claimed 43 bulls. Further hunts were allowed. In October 1965, 50 of the 329 tule elk in Owens Valley were shot. Although such shooting was meant to cull out the poorer specimens, calves—and healthy adult elk—were sometimes killed.

People concerned with the fate of the animals formed the Committee for the Preservation of the Tule Elk, the main objectives being the end of such hunts and the creation of a permanent, wild sanctuary for the elk. This was achieved finally in March, 1967, when the City of Los Angeles (which owns most of Owens Valley) set the area aside as a permanent wildlife refuge. At latest count there were 290 tule elk in Owens Valley, and 34 on the Tupman reserve.

Much less fortunate was another native elk, the Merriam (or Arizona) elk. This elk, now extinct, once lived in certain mountain areas of New Mexico and Arizona. Though its range was a narrow one, the elk was abundant. Hunted down partly because of its delicious flesh, partly because it competed with livestock for food on the ranges, its numbers dwindled steadily. By 1896 it was extremely rare. In 1906, hunters destroyed the last herd in the Chiricahua Mountains of Arizona.

Even the most ardent conservationists admit that there are cases where selective hunting becomes necessary, when natural predators have been eliminated. Hunts of this kind are sponsored by those in charge of game management, as in the fall of 1966 on the Aransas National Wildlife Refuge in Texas.

This refuge is the winter nesting grounds of the last wild whooping cranes, which in December, 1967 numbered forty-eight birds. In January, 1968, a hunter shot one of these, and though the bird was rushed to a veterinary hospital in San Antonio, Texas, it died of its wounds. Many other birds live on the refuge, too, and a variety of mammals including deer. For years the number of deer increased until in 1966 there were an estimated 14,000, far too many for the flat, grassy expanse of the refuge's 47,000 plus acres to support. So, the Fish and Wildlife Service, in cooperation with state officials, provided for a carefully-controlled hunting season on bucks only, and only by bow and arrow. On the night of October 1, and in the early morning hours, line on line of cars bearing hunters headed toward the admission gate of the Aransas refuge. By four A.M. when the gate opened, a column of cars nearly three miles long stretched along the highway. Before the month-long season was over, 3500 archers, their clothes and faces camouflaged to make them less visible against the grass and trees, hunted and brought down a total of 135 bucks. This was far fewer than the wildlife managers had hoped for and it may be that hunters with guns will be permitted to hunt in the future.

The most common deer of the west is the mule deer. Its abundant, eastern cousin is the whitetail deer, a reddish brown deer with a large, wagging tail which is white on its underside. The mule deer's rounded, white tail is naked on the underside and has a black tip; his large, twitching ears are what have given him his name. This deer was given complete protection on the Kaibab Plateau on the north rim of the Grand Canyon, the area being declared a National Game Preserve in 1906. At the same time, federal hunters killed off predators in the area to help neighboring ranchers protect their livestock. In twenty-five years, the hunters killed 781 mountain lions and 5000 coyotes. The result was that the Kaibab mule deer increased from 4000 to 100,000 by 1924. Hungrily seeking food, they nibbled every leaf and grass blade and branch until ninety percent of the vegetation was gone. The Kaibab range was increasingly strewn with the bodies of starved deer. By 1940 their numbers had decreased by starvation and disease to fewer than 15,000. Now hunters have been permitted to keep the population down to a size that the land can support.

A small, beautiful creature of the rodent family shares the Kaibab range with the mule deer. This is the Kaibab squirrel, with tall, tufted ears, dark fur, and snowy white tail. The Kaibab squirrel is presently on the government's "rare and endangered" list. Nevertheless, the Director of the Interior Department's Bureau of Sport Fisheries and Wildlife, John S. Gottschalk, stated in the fall of 1966, ". . . some surplus of the squirrels may exist and, if so, it may be advisable to permit hunters to harvest the surplus." This statement immediately brought an outcry from those who believe that the whole federal and state program of predator control are what causes the problem. Mr. Gottschalk was accused in a *New York Times* editorial of promoting gunning rather than conservation.

Whatever the outcome of the continuing conflict between different philosophies of game management and preservation, it is clear that man has upset the ecological balance of nature and that once this has happened it is extremely difficult to restore it. The wolf and the mountain lion probably can never be brought back to help hold down the deer or moose herds, so that, ironically, some species must be hunted by man "for their own good." Just possibly, Mr. Gottschalk suggests, this could happen in the case of the smallest of North American deer, known as the key deer.

This little animal stands only about two feet high at the shoulder. The key deer once occupied most of the lower Florida Keys but overhunting, development of the islands, hurricanes and fire reduced it to only some thirty in-

Key deer

dividuals by 1949. Gunners sent packs of hounds into the island thickets to drive the deer out; then as the small deer attempted to swim to other islands, shot them. The animals also crossed the highway that cuts through and across the chain of keys to Key West and were killed by automobiles —as they still are.

Protective legislation, establishment of the Key Deer Wildlife Refuge in 1953, and favorable publicity helped to save this species. The first donation of funds toward protecting the deer was made by the sportsmen's Boone and Crockett Club. The key deer appears to be slowly increasing its numbers and in 1964 its population was estimated at 300. This is certainly hopeful, compared with the earlier number of thirty, but it is no guarantee that the species will remain unless great care is taken now and in the future; in 1967 it still remained on the "endangered" list.

The caribou, another member of the deer tribe, is being steadily pressed back by civilization. In 1953, cameraman Herb Crisler and his wife Lois went to the Arctic regions of Alaska and were able to watch and photograph one of the last great caribou herds of that region. There, far from other human beings, sheltered from blizzard or rain by only a small tent, the couple watched the herds migrating across the treeless tundra. Velvet-antlered bulls with gray bodies and white collars cantered along on their slender legs, followed by the smaller-antlered cows. Luckily, the Crislers also saw the long-legged fawns (their coats are not spotted as with other deer) and captured them on film.

These caribou were free and wild, and their numbers were impressive though far fewer than when white men first came to Alaska. Then one or two million caribou roamed the land. In winter, the caribou sought out vast stands of white spruce where the forest floor was covered with lichen, a thin, slow-growing plant that spreads over rocks and tree roots. The caribou pawed through the snow to reach the lichen, their hoofs like sharp spades. The name caribou comes from the Algonquin Indian word for "shoveler."

White men's guns, whether in the hands of the whites or later of the Eskimos, blasted away at the herds. Even more destructive were the fires that swept over Alaska. During the gold-rush days, miners slashed and burned the timber. For some fifty years, millions of acres burned or were reburned each year until eighty percent of the original white spruce was gone, and with it the caribou's main supply of winter food. Whalers and fur sealers slaughtered the caribou for its meat, and also the big, shaggy musk ox. The Eskimo had much the same relation to the caribou as the Plains Indians to the bison, depending on the animals for food, shelter, clothing, and tools. With the disappearance of the caribou herds, many Eskimos were destitute. Between 1891 and 1902, well meaning white people imported about 1300 reindeer, a semi-domesticated Siberian species of deer, to start herds for the Eskimos. The reindeer took all too well to their new home and in thirty years the original herds had grown to nearly 650,000. The result was disastrous for the native caribou, and even for the reindeer

for the latter ate out the winter ranges, destroying the once rich supply of lichen. Lichen grows very slowly, and needs on an average of ten years to recover where reindeer have been.

Today, the main concentration of caribou is in the east central section of Alaska. Sometimes they migrate through parts of Mount McKinley National Park and then wander beyond the safety of the park boundaries. There is no closed season for hunting, and no limits to the number that can be shot, in most areas. (This is true, also, of the wolverine and the walrus, both increasingly rare animals.) Those concerned with the survival of the caribou urge that they need special protection if they are to remain a part of our wildlife.

The greatest organized invasion of the northern wilderness regions began in 1954 when a joint United States-Canadian project began, the construction of a 3000-mile radar warning system across arctic Canada from Alaska to Greenland to alert both nations in the event of attacks from the polar regions. This, the famous DEW line—Distant Early Warning line—brought hundreds of men and trucks, bulldozers, tractors, and airplanes into the remaining strong-

Caribou

holds of the already harassed wildlife. It also brought potential hunters for few of the men, faced with big game animals free for the shooting, could resist trying to take a prize specimen home with them.

The caribou of Alaska and Canada are called barren ground caribou. The other major type in North America is the woodland caribou, another animal treading dangerously close to the edge of extinction. Once a resident of the northern forests in the United States, through northern Maine, New Hampshire, and the Candian border region across Minnesota, the only place the woodland caribou can be seen today is in the Superior Roadless Area of Minnesota's Superior National Forest. A few small herds still remain in parts of Canada.

Thanks to last minute protection, we can still see herds of pronghorn "antelopes" on the western plains. These lithe creatures are found only in North America. Other hoofed animals such as elk and deer migrated to this country in prehistoric times across the land bridge of the Bering Strait, or, as in the case of the horse, were brought here by man. The graceful white and chestnut pronghorn with its black, erect horns, is the fleetest of our mammals, and can attain a speed of sixty miles per hour. Another distinctive trait of pronghorns are the long white hairs on their buttocks. By erecting these hairs in the sunlight they can flash brilliant white signals of danger to other pronghorns as far away as several miles.

Once, the pronghorns covered the western plains in great numbers, possibly as many as forty million. In the days before Indians had horses to ride, only a few were killed. Even after the arrival of the horse, the pronghorns often outdistanced their pursuers. But the increasing tide of armed hunters, combined with the pronghorn's wide-eyed curiosity, resulted in more and more of the animals being

Mountain goat

killed. By 1910 there were only a few scattered bands. Emergency protective measures kept them from being on the extinct list today. There are now free-roaming herds in Nevada, Wyoming, and Montana, and there are specified hunting seasons. They also exist in national parks and wild-life refuges, particularly the Sheldon National Antelope Refuge in Nevada, and the Hart Mountain National Antelope Refuge in Oregon. It would seem that the once-vanishing pronghorns are now safe.

The same cannot be said of another hoofed animal. This exceedingly rare mammal, often called the "old man of the mountain" is the mountain goat. These mountain climbers with their yellowish white coats and dark horns seek the highest peaks, and only hardy hunters pursue them. Aside from man, they are comparatively safe from enemies. Avalanches are a danger, and rain is a threat because if their wooly fleece becomes soaked they are subject to inflammation of the lungs. It is estimated that there are no more than around 1200 mountain goats in the national parks of Montana and Washington, with perhaps a few thousand in the Canadian Rockies.

Watching caribou, wolverines, grizzlies, and gray wolves in the Alaskan arctic, Lois Crisler expressed what all lovers of wildlife feel when she said, "Wilderness without animals is mere scenery."

6 Fins, Fur, and Toads

Against the gray of the Antarctic sky, a fleet of fifteen ships moves slowly southward through the open sea. Here and there, breaking the monotony of the cold, gray water are drifting icebergs that have broken off the Antarctic continent in the region of the Weddell Sea. The ships in the fleet are of varying size and are spread out over a one-hundred-mile-wide area, each ship having a different job to do. The ships are equipped with short wave radios by which the scattered crews communicate. There are a thousand men on this expedition and all have one goal in mind. Whales. For it is here at the edges of the pack ice that the majority of the great, air-breathing sea-dwellers are found: fin whales, sperm whales, humpback, and blue.

The largest ship, the heart of the fleet, resembles a high-riding tanker, its decks covered with winches and derricks. This is the factory ship where the whales are hauled on board and processed. Other ships in the fleet include a tanker that carries fuel oil, a freezer ship to carry frozen whale meat, two ferry boats, and finally the smaller ships called catchers which retrieve the carcasses of killed whales and tow them to the factory ship.

Now, in February, the man in the high crow's nest aboard the factory ship, scans the water. Even though blue whales are scarce, who knows when one may appear to add to the whales already taken? The captain on the bridge keeps an eye out too, and even the helmsman. Every patch of foam begins to seem like the "blow" of a whale. The top gunner waits near his powerful harpoon gun.

Suddenly, the man in the crow's nest calls out. There, in the near distance, is a blue whale, the great slate-blue back arching out of the water briefly before it makes a shallow dive. The gunner, his green, waterproof suit shining from spray, swings his heavy gun. He knows the swimming pattern of the blue whale and how to time the firing of the harpoon at exactly the right moment. There is no hurry. The whale, over seventy feet long, and therefore of legal size, has just come up from a long, deep dive. Now it will go through a number of shallow dives lasting only twelve to fifteen seconds each. If it lingers an extra moment on the surface, breathing in the air essential to its life, the harpoon will find it. Or even if it makes its deep dive again, one that may last from ten to twenty minutes, the whale is doomed for it cannot stay under water forever. Though it may recognize the danger, it cannot outrace the ship. It will merely exhaust itself, its dives becoming shorter and shallower.

The gunner spreads his legs and stoops, measuring the range, waiting for the big blue to surface once more. Now. He fires. The harpoon streaks across the water, striking the waves a little short of the whale. It is equipped with a grenade timed to go off in four seconds. There is a dull thud as the grenade explodes, and a writhing convulsion of the whale's body just before the huge creature dives in an attempt to escape the danger and the pain. The chief engineer at the whale winch goes to work, letting the line, attached to the harpoon, go out unchecked at first, then applying the powerful brake. He plays the blue giant like an angler playing a game trout. Finally, a hundred yards away the whale surfaces with a tremendous blast, gulping air for another dive. But now a killer harpoon, without a line, is in the gun. The ship speeds forward to within twenty yards. The gunner fires and strikes the giant squarely behind the head. The smoke clears and the blue whale rolls over, dead, its light colored belly shining in the February sunshine.

A moment before, it was a living creature. Now as men and machines go to work it has changed to a commodity, a thing to be turned into oil, margarine, meat, vitamin extracts, fertilizer, dog and cat food.

The blue whale—sometimes called the sulphur-bottomed whale because of the greenish cast of its belly under water— is the largest living creature on earth. Possibly it is the largest creature that ever lived, including even the largest of the prehistoric dinosaurs. It can be over one hundred feet long, although the average is less, and can weigh 150 tons or more. Its giant heart alone can weigh over 1000 pounds, its liver almost a ton, and its mighty tongue nearly 9000 pounds. Yet, today, this mightiest of creatures is on the verge of extinction.

Like other whales, the blue is a mammal, meaning that the young are born alive and are suckled on the mother's milk. Grizzlies and mice are mammals. So is man. A blue whale's newborn calf is some twenty-five feet long and may weigh more than an adult elephant. The calf may nurse a full six months. Blue whales are not fast breeders. It takes nearly eleven months for the baby whale to develop within the mother whale's body. Most of the remaining blue whales live in the southern hemisphere at the edge of the Antarctic ice packs. In winter they head for subtropical waters to bear their young. Whereas most other whales tend to travel in groups called pods, the blue whales usually travel alone or in pairs.

The familiar cry of whalemen, "There she blows!" indicates that a lookout has sighted the so-called spout of a whale. This spout is actually air that the whale blows from its lungs when it surfaces. The warm, expelled breath forms a whitish vapor in the same way that human being's breath mists in winter. With large whales, the geyser-like plume may rise ten or twenty feet into the air and be seen from miles away.

Blue whale

Nobody knows exactly how many of the giant blues once swam the seas, ranging through both the Atlantic and the Pacific, north and south, but the numbers must have been great for men have pursued them for centuries. Long ago, when whales of many kinds were still abundant around coastal waters, various whales were hunted from land, in small boats. The Basques hunted them along the shores of

the Bay of Biscay for nearly one thousand years, and even a hundred years ago whales could still be taken off the Scottish coast. Gradually, the whales retreated to more distant waters. Today, modern whaling is limited almost exclusively to the Antarctic, and the chief whaling nations are Japan, Norway, and the Soviet Union. Once, the United States was the greatest whaling nation in the world.

When the first white colonists settled on the island the Indians called "Nantucket," they watched in amazement as the Indians pursued whales in their flimsy canoes. The red men were armed only with wooden harpoons to which a sharpened stone or bone was fastened, and yet they set out boldly on the choppy waters of bays and inlets whenever the whales came into the coastal waters in search of food. The canoes, each carrying two Indians, would surround one of the large sea beasts. At the right moment, the harpooner in the prow of each canoe rose and sent his barbed shaft into the whale's glistening back. A dozen or more of the harpoons might pierce the creature's hide, each harpoon bearing a length of rope made of greased fiber behind it. These ropes were kept afloat by means of inflated bladders made from carefully-sewn deer skin. As the whale plunged downward, thrashing against the harpoons, it very often fouled the floating lines, or its lashing tail upset some of the canoes. It was a risky business for the American red men, but a whale's carcass was considered well worth it because of its tons of meat, blubber, and bone.

The majority of the colonists at Nantucket, Maine, as well as along the other parts of the Eastern seaboard in the early 1600s, knew little about whaling. But they learned quickly enough how desirable whale oil was for burning in their lamps. They saw, also, how the Indians used every part of the whale for one purpose or another, and very soon the colonists joined with the Indians in the whale hunts. It was one of the rare instances in our history where the white man and the Indian worked together for the advantage of both.

Once a whale was dragged to shore, the whole settlement crowded around it and helped to cut it up. Depending upon the size of the settlement, and the size of the whale, this could take a week or more. Usually the whale involved was a black right whale, which might be sixty feet long. Each year, the Indians—and then the white men—watched for the big blacks to come lazily swimming down along the eastern seaboard in the fall, then in the spring move back northward to their cool-water, summer homes. During the migrations, the whales would often enter bays and inlets where they became targets for men in canoes or small boats. But they did not always come close enough,

Right whale

or escaped when pursued. The Indians had learned they could not depend on having a regular supply of the black right whales so they hunted the smaller whales and porpoises that came to river mouths and gulfs. Eventually, this "little whale" industry, and that of whaling generally, was taken over by the white man.

In 1849, New Bedford, Massachusetts, was the most important whaling seaport in the world. There, at the mouth of the Acushnet River, a forest of masts and rigging rose from crowds of sailing ships. Everywhere there stood rows of crudely built barrels full of whale oil. In the narrow passages left between the barrels, sailors and ship's officers of all races made their way to and from the various vessels. Some wore wooden shoes, some went barefoot; most had beards and long hair; others might have shaven heads, filed teeth, and wear earrings. There were Dutch sailors, Russian, Norwegian, British, African, Chinese, all speaking different languages. Whatever the language, talk centered on whales. The species they valued most was the sperm whale, a whale of the deep ocean waters, tough and dangerous but a living tank of the finest whale oil and a substance called spermaceti. This spermaceti, a light waxy substance, was used for candles. Another extremely valuable product then and now, was ambergris, a gray, waxy material used as the base for expensive perfumes.

One reason that the New England whalers set out to hunt the big sperm whale was that the once-abundant right whales had been hunted almost to the vanishing point along the coast. Nantucket led the way in the sperm whale hunting business, building ever larger boats for longer voyages off shore. Provincetown, New Bedford, and other seaport cities all the way from Maine to Virginia were busy in their own specialized whaling pursuits. By 1774 the American ocean-going whaling fleet numbered three hundred and sixty ships, three hundred of them from Massachusetts. From Nantucket Harbor, American whalers sailed into Davis Strait and as far as Spitsbergen in the Arctic Ocean. From 1835 to 1872, in spite of the intervention of the Civil War, American whalemen took some 300,000 whales of all types. Among these was the gray whale.

The gray whale, which still migrates up and down the

Sperm whale

Pacific Coast of North America each year, often so near land that residents on the coast have formed whale-watching clubs, used to be present in great numbers. Indians and the Spanish settlers hunted them first. Then a big part of the Yankee fleet in the middle 1800s made an annual side trip to the west coast to slaughter the California gray whales. It is estimated that about 11,000 were killed between 1846 and 1875. During the next twenty years, thousands more were killed until the eastern Pacific population was nearly wiped out. Now, under complete protection, the population numbers about 10,000.

American whaling declined around 1870, as did whaling generally because of the widespread adoption of petroleum as a source of power and light in place of whale oil. Then came the steamship and the harpoon gun which made whaling far less dangerous and expensive. Norway, in particular, resumed whaling with new vigor. The explosive harpoon, invented by a Norwegian in 1864, gave the hunters a fatal edge over all whales, including the mighty blue whale. So effective was the new harpoon that in a short time the whales in the Arctic and Davis Strait were near extinction. Again whaling ceased—but only until it was discovered that there were fresh hunting grounds in the Antarctic. The slaughter began anew, and with the development of the factory ship the whales had less chance than ever to survive.

In one season, 1929–30, over 19,000 blue whales were killed. Since then the figure has steadily declined. In 1963–64 only 112 blues were taken. Partly this is because of regulations set down by the International Whaling Commission; chiefly it is because there are so few blue whales left. As of 1967, one authority placed the number of the powerful blues remaining as low as 600. Although conservationists pleaded in 1964 that all whale hunting cease for fifty years, the Commission, made up of sixteen one-time whale-hunting nations, decided in favor of continuing controlled hunting. In the meantime, headlines such as DOOMSDAY FOR THE GREAT BLUE WHALE occur regularly, and it is all too possible that such predictions will come true.

The right whale and the humpback, too, are now rare, as is the huge, blunt-headed sperm whale. It was this species of whale that was the subject of Herman Melville's great novel on American whaling, *Moby Dick*. Because of the sperm whale's dwindling numbers, scientists are at work making studies of this big, toothed whale with the hope that such studies may help save it from extinction.

In 1962, a Seattle scientist, Dale Rice, whale biologist employed by the federal government, carried on a study of the sperm whale. He and fellow workers held their own kind of whale hunts in two chartered whale catchers operating out of Richmond, California. They cruised about one hundred miles off shore, armed with specially modified shotguns loaded with "harpoons" about the size of a pencil. Whenever they were lucky enough to sight a sperm whale, they drew as close as possible and fired a harpoon into the hide behind the whale's dorsal fin. The muscle is so thick there that the whale hardly feels the shot. Each harpoon is numbered and it is the researchers' hope that whalers, and processing plant workers, will report back to them as to where the whale was caught. In this way they hope not only to estimate how many sperm whales remain, and where their wanderings take them, but provide facts useful to federal negotiators who would like to enforce more stringent regulations on the primary whaling nations, Russia, Japan, and Norway.

Whales, of course, are not specifically North American sea animals, but they have played an important part in our history. Also, the United States as a member of the International Whaling Commission, and a major world power, has a responsibility to try to save endangered species. For all that the oceans teem with other forms of life, the death of the last, mighty blue whale will leave a void that nothing else can fill.

Long before whalers turned their attention to the Antarctic regions, seal hunters were busy among the crowded rookeries of South Georgia. When Captain James Cook discovered this island of the South Atlantic east of Cape Horn, in 1775, he found there vast herds of fur seals and elephant seals. The first commercial hunters to visit the island were Americans. From the time of their arrival in 1790, the fur seal-hunting industry grew swiftly. A single vessel often returned to the United States with 50,000 skins. By 1822 these fur seal herds were so reduced that it was hardly worthwhile hunting them. The hunters turned their attention and their weapons to another abundant creature, the elephant seal.

Whereas the fur seals had been hunted for their lush pelts, the elephant seals were hunted for the large amount of oil that could be extracted from their thick layers of blubber. The elephant seal's hair is thin, its skin often peeling from its body. The male elephant seal, especially an old bull, is remarkable for his strange nose which looks somewhat like a shortened, bulbous elephant trunk. Normally the grotesque nose droops over this seal's mouth, but when he is excited he inflates his snout so that it stands out from his face. An excellent swimmer, he seeks his food in the sea. On land, elephant seals are extremely clumsy, pulling their thick bodies about by their front flippers while the hind flippers drag behind them. This awkwardness on land made the herds sunning themselves on the rocks easy prey for hunters. The story of the fur seal was repeated and the elephant seals became extremely scarce not only in the Antarctic but off the shores of our own nation.

Once, elephant seals were abundant along the coast and the islands of California and Lower California. By 1892 they were reduced to a few dozen individuals that sought refuge on Guadalupe Island, Mexico. These few survivors would

Elephant seal

probably have been exterminated quickly if there had not been a decline in the market for their oil. Left alone, the small herd increased. Then a manufacturer was inspired with the idea of canning elephant seal meat for cat and dog food. He obtained a permit for his operations from the Mexican government, and the slaughter began once more. Before the big-nosed seal could be exterminated, strong protests were made and the Mexican government did not renew the canner's permit. Instead, it created protective laws so that today the great bulls with their harems are beginning to return to their old breeding grounds along the southern California coast.

Like the fur seal of the South Polar regions, the fur seals of Alaska became the victims of hunters from the time the Russians discovered that vast land and its islands. When a Russian navigator and explorer, Gerassim Pribilof, landed on the island he named St. George, he discovered the summer breeding grounds of the seal called the "sea bear." The beaches were covered with countless thousands of these small-eared seals. There were blackish bulls, grayish cows, and fat, soft-haired pups, so many that there was scarcely room for a man to walk among them. A year later it was discovered that a neighboring island, St. Paul, was even more heavily populated with fur seals than St. George. The next twenty years saw the greatest mass slaughter in the history of the fur trade. It came to a halt when it appeared that the seals faced extinction, a halt that lasted only until the herds had multiplied again. Thereafter, the Russian authorities decreed that only mature bulls could be killed, leaving the females and pups free to build up the herds.

This system worked so well that the fur seal trade flourished for many years, though there were again times when overhunting, especially of the illegal kind, threatened the herds. One kind of hunting, called pelagic sealing, developed. In this, companies without hunting permits shot the fur seals on the high seas, killing both males and females recklessly. Only about one seal out of five shot was recovered from the water. British and Canadian sealers did much of this kind of hunting after Alaska was an American territory, and this nearly led to an international crisis. In 1911, Britain and the United States agreed to a treaty whereby pelagic hunting was outlawed, just in time to prevent the extermination of the northern fur seals. The United States began a careful program of conservation with the result that the fur seals are abundant. Canada and the United States share the Pribilof Islands herd, culling only a specified number of three-year-old males each year from an estimated two million animals. Revenues from the furs have repaid the original purchase price of Alaska several times over.

The future of another American animal that spends part of its time in water is much more doubtful. This is the American crocodile. Compared to the alligator, which lives in fresh water and is present in a number of southeastern wildlife refuges (though increasingly threatened even there), the crocodile is a dweller of shoal salt water along the shores of Florida Bay. It differs from the alligator, also, in its lighter color, the protruding teeth of its lower jaw, and its long, narrow, pointed snout. Unlike its African relative, the American crocodile is not a man-eater and avoids human beings when it can. Its tough hide is popular for shoes and women's handbags. Although the crocodile was probably never very abundant, its present range is much more limited than formerly and unless it is given more protection than it now has it may become only a creature of the zoos.

American crocodile

The alligator has always been more numerous than the crocodile, but in February, 1967, its survival had become so imperiled that Senator George A. Smathers of Florida introduced a bill in the Senate to protect this creature. Like the crocodile, the alligator is a kind of "living fossil" and so is one of the few remaining links with the prehistoric world. In spite of law enforcement efforts by the National Park Service, poachers managed to kill over 1000 alligators in the Everglades National Park alone, in 1966. The number of alligators taken from Louisiana swamps and rivers is estimated at 15,000 and 30,000 a year. The hides, when made into suitcases and shoes, bring high prices. Recent surveys made by rangers show that in less than ten years the alligator population has dropped by as much as three-fourths.

Another increasingly rare creature is the green turtle. The green turtle occurs worldwide but it has been greatly reduced on the mainland United States by those who hunt it

and its eggs. This large marine turtle is on the endangered
list of the Bureau of Sport Fisheries and Wildlife.

Also in trouble is the Texas tortoise that lives in the
southern reaches of Texas and feeds there on the cactus
plants, its favorite food. As of 1967, two firms in Laredo
were exporting about 10,000 tortoises a year to other states,
mostly as pets. The majority die in captivity. Others are
converted into turtle oil to be used in cosmetic creams.
State biologists say that unless the tortoise is given protection, the species may become extinct. The Texas legis-
lature in 1967 took steps to enact a law against commercial
exploitation of the Texas tortoise.

The new law would extend protection to still another
native of the dry lands of the Southwest, the horned toad.
This spiny, fierce-looking but harmless animal has been
carried out of Texas and neighboring states by the thousands, chiefly by souvenir hunters. Like the tortoise, most
die in captivity. One firm went into the business of drying

Green turtle

horned toads and making them into stickpins. A living
horned toad may not be the most beautiful little creature
in the world but he is certainly more attractive and useful
alive than adorning somebody's necktie. Scuttling about in
the hot, dry climates he likes best, he is a marvelous de-
stroyer of insects, many of which are pests.

The worlds of whales and horned toads, crocodiles and
seals are far apart but each species contributes its special
quality to the over-all world of nature, of which man
himself is a part.

7   Refugees and Refuges

The Land Rover sped across the southern African plains, its tires roiling up dust. Riding on the outside of the specially outfitted car was a man with a lasso. Ahead, hoofs pounding, ran a large, tawny animal with spiral shaped horns. Swift though the animal was, the Land Rover was swifter. In a moment the vehicle roared alongside the elk-like creature. The man with the rope tossed it and the noose whisked through the air, hovered, then settled down cleanly around the big bull's neck. The car stopped and the other men leaped out, hauling at the rope to pull the animal down. In a few minutes they were joined by a truck carrying more helpers and a large, wooden crate. After much pushing and hauling, the men managed to force the powerful animal into the wooden cage. Then they stood back, congratulating themselves, and admiring their captive.

The animal, five feet tall at the shoulder, his pale tawny hide relieved on the flanks by vertical white stripes, was a greater kudu, one of the most sought after forms of African big game. A member of the antelope family, the kudu is fleet and is an excellent jumper, able to clear an eight-foot fence from a standing position. His large ears are so keen it is very difficult for hunters to approach close to him, and he is also very adept at keeping to cover among trees and bushes. An adult bull carries beautiful spiraling horns that

Kudu

can measure up to sixty-six inches (the record) along the
curves. His weight may reach 650 pounds. The female is
smaller and hornless. The kudus do not travel in herds in
open country but generally associate in small groups, mostly
females and young, with perhaps one old bull.

The men in the Land Rover were not hunters in the usual
sense. Rather, they were rescuers. The kudu, like many
other big game animals in Africa, has been hunted to the
point of extermination. Several years ago, an American,
Dr. Frank C. Hibben, a professor at Albuquerque, New
Mexico, and a member of that state's Game and Fish Commission, became concerned with the kudu's plight. In 1962
he suggested that the commission purchase eight of the

animals and transport them to New Mexico to see if they could survive and breed there. The commissioners agreed to the experiment and arrangements were made to capture and ship the kudus to the United States.

A native exporter in Africa rounded up fifteen kudus (some destined for other zoos), loaded them in trucks, and drove them toward a quarantine station where they would have to remain for two months while quarantine officials made sure they harbored no dangerous disease germs. On the way to the quarantine station there was a cloudburst and a flash flood washed out the road in front of one of the trucks. The truck overturned and three of the precious kudus were killed. The exporter turned back to try to find replacements but he was unsuccessful.

Following the two-month quarantine period, the kudus were loaded onto a ship and lashed to the deck in crates. Again trouble pursued them, stormy weather chasing the ship for much of the journey. At last, the big antelopes arrived at Clifton, New Jersey where they spent another month under quarantine at the U. S. Department of Agriculture station there. After this there was a five-day truck trip across country for the eight kudus destined for Albuquerque; they arrived there in December, 1963.

The kudu is not the first imported animal to be deliberately adopted by the United States. Back in 1951, the New Mexico Department of Game and Fish began its program of introducing exotic species. The first animal it encouraged was the Barbary sheep from Algeria. The animal was already present in the United States, in zoos or in the hands of private collectors. The New Mexico wildlife specialists assembled fifty-two of the large, horned sheep and released them in rugged terrain in the state's Canadian River Canyon. In 1955, the Game Commission authorized a hunting season for the sheep. Other hunting seasons followed but were temporarily stopped when the herd suffered a setback in 1961 and 1962 from extremely hard winters. In 1966 the herd numbered around 1500—considerably more than the 200 or 300 native Rocky Mountain bighorn sheep in the state—and hunting resumed. There is always an element of risk in introducing foreign or so-called "exotic" animals into a new environment as the introduced animals may compete with or endanger native animals. According to the New Mexico State Game Commission, such dangers can be minimized, or completely avoided, with careful controls. Current plans of this agency call for establishing a captive herd of desert bighorn sheep with the hope that plantings from such a herd can be made in suitable bighorn areas in the state and thereby increase the bighorn population.

Like the kudu, another rare antelope has been brought to this country in an attempt to save the species. This is the Arabian oryx, a beautiful desert animal that lived and thrived in the sandy wastes and gravel plains of the Arabian peninsula. A sandy gray color, this oryx has dark line markings on its face and forelegs. Its long, sharp horns curve backward from its forehead like brown scimitars. Across the loose-shifting sands of North Africa and Arabia, the oryx travels with comparative ease thanks to large, spreading hoofs, and an ability to go for long stretches of time without water.

For centuries the oryx managed to survive, in spite of the encroachment of man, in a climate so harsh that few other animals occurred there. Local Bedouin tribes, once they had firearms, began taking a steady toll of these long-horned beasts. The greatest destruction, however, has come in recent years. Organized hunting parties in automobiles, many of them made up of British and American oil company employees, shot the animals for excitement. Native

Arabian oryx

rulers, too, have been indifferent to their natural heritage, even arranging hunts in which royalty riddled the herds with machine guns.

In May, 1963, four Arabian oryx traveled through New York on their way to the Maytag Zoo in Phoenix, Arizona. They were so rare by that time that it required the co-operative effort of several nations to arrange for their arrival: the United States, England, Kenya, and the Aden Protectorate. One group alone, the World Wildlife Fund, originated in London, contributed over $6,000 to "Operation Oryx" which in turn was managed by England's Fauna Preservation Society. In order to capture the rare and elusive animals, aircraft, custom-equipped capturing cars, and trained zoologists and hunters were needed.

The Phoenix Zoo was chosen as a likely place to try to save the oryx because the climate is similar to that of Saudi Arabia. In 1963, the first calf was born at the zoo. Since then additional adult oryx have reached Phoenix and more calves have been produced. Still, there was some concern among the zoo officials because most of the calves were males. Then, in September of 1966, a female calf was born. In January, 1967, another female arrived and zoologists relaxed a little, while newspapers reported the good news nationally. The outlook for the oryx seems promising but it is by no means certain that this graceful antelope is completely safe. As of 1967, the Phoenix herd numbered sixteen—more than half of the world's recorded oryx population! When any species is reduced to such a small number, not only extreme care but luck is required to save it.

Wildlife managers hope that eventually some of these introduced species (including the Siberian ibex, and the horned South African gemsbok, also adopted by the New Mexico Game and Fish Department) may become established as American game animals. The wild European boar, let loose in the mountains of North Carolina and Tennessee in 1912, and also in New Hampshire, has flourished and mixed with feral swine and is a favorite target for sportsmen. The introduction of some alien creatures can have very unfortunate consequences, as in the case of the carp. The first carp were shipped to this country in 1879. They were

South African gemsbok

so happy in their new homeland that they took over, and millions of dollars have since been spent in an effort to remove them from rivers and streams.

Transplanting wildlife from one country to another cannot be done recklessly. Among those interested in the careful transfer of threatened animals to new refuges is the World Wildlife Fund which operates in nine countries, including the United States. One of the group's main objectives is to procure money to buy land for suitable preserves.

At the same time, the fight goes on to save our own rare animals.

A recently established haven is a 300-acre federal preserve halfway between Baltimore, Maryland, and Washington, D.C. for the perpetuation of almost extinct animals native to the United States. Here, within the larger Patuxent Wildlife Research Center, scientists hope to "teach" endangered animals how to live in a changing world. If the animals learn well, they will be released back into the wilds or into parks where anti-hunting laws are enforced. The scientists also hope to develop animals with a high degree of inborn wariness and wildness, through selective breeding. In the spring of 1966, biologists began the first phase of the rare-and-endangered-species program, working out in the field, studying the animals in their natural habitats, and gathering species for shipment to the Patuxent Center. Among mammals, the black-footed ferret is high on the list for study. According to the U. S. Department of the Interior, supervising the Patuxent Center, seventy-eight species native to this country are in some degree of danger. Half of the estimated forty animals and birds in the world that have become extinct in the last 150 years, met their fate since 1900. So, emergency action is needed if others are not to go down the road to oblivion.

Although uncontrolled hunting has been the main factor in destruction of most animal species, even constructive projects such as dams and irrigation canals can be a serious threat to wildlife. One of the most dramatic instances of this happened when the mighty Kariba Dam was built across

the Zambezi River separating Northern and Southern Rho-
desia in Africa. The dam began operation in 1959. Eventually the waters backed up by this dam formed a lake
large enough to cover Long Island in New York. Unfortunately, it also covered hills and valleys where numerous African animals (and human beings) had their homes.
It is impossible to estimate how many animals were
drowned, or marooned on hills that became isolated islands
as the waters steadily rose. Animals *dependent* on water,
such as crocodiles and fish, perished too when water was
diverted from the river bed.

Around the time the dam first began backing up the
waters, a project called "Operation Noah" was launched
in Britain to help African game wardens rescue the threatened elephants, buffaloes, lions, and antelopes, as well as
birds, and transport them to new reserves established in
the area. Persons from many countries gave not only money
and time but bundles of women's nylon hose! The stockings
were ideal for making soft, nonchafing ropes to use in tying
down struggling animals so that they could be carried to
safety. Men of various nationalities volunteered to work in
the heat under circumstances that were often filled with
danger. Working in small boats, or on land, transporting
captured animals by truck, or forcing them to swim alongside a launch, the rescue teams fought valiantly against the
widening lake created by the dam. They were only a handful in the face of what needed to be done and although they
succeeded in rescuing around 6000 animals, many thousands more perished.

Dams have frequently caused problems for animal life in
our own country, even those not built on a gigantic scale.
In north central Nebraska is the Ainsworth Canal, built to
take water from Merritt Dam for irrigation. During 1965
and 1966 a survey revealed that 261 deer were trapped in

the deep, fifty-three-mile-long concrete-lined trough, a surprisingly high number as deer are not abundant in the area. Some of these animals were discovered in time to be rescued but many others drowned or were so crippled from their attempts to struggle up the smooth walls, they had to be destroyed. Some of the deer had worn their knees to the bone in their repeated struggles to climb out. Other animals trapped in the canal included snakes, box turtles, a beaver, two muskrats, one mink, a porcupine, and a coyote.

Although such canals often carry water to desert areas and thereby benefit wildlife, especially if the canal is an earthen ditch from which an animal has hope of escape, they also present dangers such as the above. An additional danger can be the presence of poisonous pesticides or chemical fertilizers.

The proposed Rampart Canyon Dam in Alaska is one which has aroused the fears of many concerned with wildlife resources. As envisioned, Rampart Dam would bestride the Yukon River about seventy-five miles northwest of Fairbanks in central Alaska, and would be the largest concrete dam in history. It would back up water to form the twelfth largest lake on earth, larger even than Lake Erie. Primarily, the dam would be built to generate electric power; secondarily for flood control.

In 1964, sixteen conservation organizations working under the auspices of the Natural Resources Council of America, made a grant to the University of Michigan to finance a study of the effects of such a dam. The report questioned the need or usefulness of the dam in any case. It would cut off up to fifty percent of the Yukon's salmon run, a blow to the fishing industry and to the Indians who depend on the salmon for food. Worse, the lake would flood out seven million acres of waterfowl breeding grounds. Animals displaced by the dam would include 5000 moose, two herds of caribou, some black and grizzly bears, and countless smaller creatures. Five million acres of forest land would be flooded. Aside from the millions of birds, mammals, and fish that would be lost, the whole unique ecological system of the Yukon Flats area would be destroyed.

Wildlife and ecology are often disregarded when man changes and rebuilds the landscape. In 1949, a flood control district was set up in central and southern Florida. The U. S. Army Corps of Engineers built a network of canals, levees, dams, pumping stations and control centers that affected the ecological balance of the area. From the central part of Florida, water flows into Lake Okeechobee and from there seeps south and southwest across broad areas of sawgrass dotted with small hills or "hammocks" that bear trees and shrubs. Seminole Indians lived on these hammocks for generations, as did animals and birds. The slowly flowing water across this "sea of grass" finally reaches Florida Bay where it mixes with ocean water to form a combination of salt and fresh water ideal for many kinds of shoal creatures. The diversion of the fresh water means a drastic change in this broad estuarine belt considered one of the richest in the world. Scientists at the Marine Institute in Miami state that the increasing salt level means death to the young and eggs of nearly all marine species. Crocodiles, already a rare species, are within the threatened area.

The diversion of the water has had dramatic effects on the Everglades National Park at the southern tip of Florida. Since 1947 this has been one of our country's foremost bird sanctuaries, and a refuge for whitetail deer, black bears, bobcats, and the rare sea mammal, the manatee. Mountain lions are present but rare. For centuries the park area, over 2300 square miles of marsh, hammocks covered by dense growth, upland areas of pine and palm, and salt-water fringes of mangroves, has been nourished and sustained by the natural southward flow of water. When the Army Engineers decided to divert the water from Lake Okeechobee into drainage control canals, this left the park to get most of its water from local rain. It took only a few years of drought for the park to begin drying up. Marshes, dying under the hot sun, were scourged with fire. Sloughs turned into flats of cracked mud. Vegetation on the hammocks withered. By the summer of 1965 the park, and its wildlife, seemed doomed. The first relief came with heavy rainfall in the fall of 1965, followed by more rain in the spring, part of it coming from hurricane Alma. By June, park superintendents were optimistic about the future of the sanctuary, although admitting that it would take time for fish and animals to come back to anywhere near their former numbers.

More rain fell in record-shattering amounts. Pumping stations and floodgates could not cope with the rising waters. Animals, especially nervous and easily-frightened deer, were being marooned on the lower hammocks. The Florida Game and Fresh Water Commission began rescue operations using "airboats" (flat bottomed craft equipped with an airplane engine and propeller in the rear) and helicopters to find the deer. After locating a stranded deer, the men would capture it, give it a tranquilizer shot, haul it up into the boat, and then carry it to higher ground. Some of the deer could not be saved; others died of shock and fright during the rescue attempts. News media reported the story of Operation Deerlift nationally.

Less than a year later, May 1967, the Everglades National Park was again newsworthy. The park was drying up again! Once more, as a result of scant rainfall (and the siphoning off of the natural water flow), fire plagued the dried hammocks, and wild creatures desperately sought out the few drying water holes left. The Tamiami Trail, which borders the park to the north, was strewn with the bodies of animals from the park trying to reach canals where they were easy prey for poachers. Man has little control of the weather but it would appear that mechanical interference with the natural pattern of the water flow in central and southern Florida could turn out to be disastrous for this unique wildlife refuge.

Balance in nature is like a long chain, each particle of life contributing to an over-all stability and well-being. Or it could be pictured as an all embracing web. When a link in the chain, or a strand in the web is removed, the entire design is altered, sometimes disastrously.

Animal life, as well as human life, is disrupted or destroyed by war, military exercises, and nuclear bomb testing. Animals in many countries were accidental victims of gunfire and bombings in both World Wars. So far, the United States has not been subjected to foreign bombs or missiles. In Vietnam, however, where United States military forces are fighting today, the once rich wildlife of that country is suffering. Tigers, elephants, and many smaller creatures have been wounded or killed. Chemical sprays designed to defoliate the jungles have injured and killed the birds and animals that live there. According to the director of Saigon's zoo in South Vietnam, in a statement made in 1967, the wild elephants in Central Vietnam have become so terrified by bombs and artillery they appear to have stopped breeding.

In 1966, a California zoologist showed that the amount of deadly strontium 90, a by-product of nuclear bomb testing, was fifty times greater in the bones of young deer in Mendicino County than in 1950. Though the amount was considered well below the danger level it shows how closely the life of animals and that of man is related. In the Aleutian Islands, when Project Long Shot culminated in the fall of 1965, biologists had to take steps to attempt to scare away the sea otters there so that they would not be endangered by a powerful underground nuclear test explosion.

Many other activities of man, from building freeways to draining swamps, affect the well-being of wild creatures. We are only beginning to understand some of the complex relations of animal life in relation to environment. Tragic mistakes have been made, and are still being made, but there appears to be a growing awareness that protection of wildlife results in the enrichment of human life.

Our National Wildlife Refuges, federal lands and waters dedicated to wildlife conservation, administered by the Bureau of Sport Fisheries and Wildlife in the Department of the Interior, are increasingly vital for the future of our wild animals and birds. The same is true of our National Parks, National Forests, Seashores, and Monuments, and of State and County preserves. It is only in such protected areas that most of our rare wildlife has any chance of survival. But constantly there is pressure from many sides, especially commercial interests, to slice off a portion of refuges or parks for purposes that work against the preservation of wildlife. What is needed is more room for our threatened wildlife species, not less. Unless more refuges are established, or present ones maintained and in many cases expanded, certain species have little chance to win out in the struggle for existence.

Private organizations and individuals have contributed greatly to the preservation of wildlife, purchasing animal sanctuaries, working for protective legislation, and educating the public to the need for even greater conservation efforts. Among the vigorous champions of our wild animals is the Defenders of Wildlife, a nonprofit organization made up of private citizens. One of the group's objectives is a crusade against roadside zoos. Too many of these are operated by persons who have little concern for and knowledge about the caged animals they exhibit to tourists for a fee. Captive wild creatures often suffer a living death in small cages, poorly fed, constantly terrified by the presence of tourists staring at them or teasing them. The tourists, too, are victims; they pay a dime or a dollar to look at the "FEROCIOUS WOLF" or the "BLOOD THIRSTY BOBCAT," and find themselves looking at a half-starved or sick creature who has no hope of ever running free again.

One day, near the beginning of our present century, a number of huge, earth-moving machines rumbled across an island at the entrance to Long Island Sound, New York. The machines began grading the island in preparation for the building of fortifications. Whether or not the workers noticed certain small creatures scurrying away from the metal claws and blades of the machines, they would not have been apt to pause, for the fleeing, tumbling creatures were merely meadow mice. After a week, the meadow mice had vanished. Every one had been buried alive under the freshly overturned and re-piled earth. The little creature was the Gull Island meadow mouse, one of the barely noticed names on the list of our extinct animals.

Only those who appreciate the value of every form of life are able to mourn the loss of a certain subspecies of mouse. How many will mourn even if the mightiest creature of all, the blue whale, joins the little meadow mouse on the list of creatures gone forever? How many are even aware that there is any danger to the blue whale, or to the wolf, the mountain lion, the caribou, the wolverine, or the polar bear? Perhaps if more people realized the threat to these animals who have contributed so much beauty, adventure, and economic value to the American scene, more would join in the effort to save them. Part of the task of conservationists is to make sure that people do know.

More and more people *are* working at the job today, here and in other parts of the world. Some day, perhaps war among human beings will cease. Some day, too, the "war" against wild animals may end. Instead of guns, we will take only cameras or field glasses to the wilderness areas that we have saved. There, watching quietly, waiting, we may win the finest trophy of all—the sight of a shy, wild creature looking back at us, neither grateful nor hostile, but simply alive, safe, and free.

Books for Further Reading

THE ALIEN ANIMALS: The Story of Imported Wildlife. George Laycock, The Natural History Press, 1966

ARCTIC WILD. Lois Crisler, Harper & Brothers, 1958

THE BEAST THAT WALKS LIKE A MAN. Harold McCracken, Hanover House, 1955

THE BUFFALO HUNTERS: THE STORY OF THE HIDE MEN. Mari Sandoz, Hastings House, 1954

EXPLORING OUR NATIONAL WILDLIFE REFUGES. Devereux Butcher, Houghton Mifflin Co., 1963

HUNTERS OF THE STORMY SEA. Harold McCracken, Doubleday & Co., 1957

LAST CHANCE ON EARTH: A REQUIEM FOR WILDLIFE. Roger A. Caras, Chilton Books, 1966

THE LIVING WILDERNESS. Rutherford Montgomery, Dodd, Mead & Co., 1964

OPERATION NOAH. Charles Lagus, Coward McCann, Inc., 1960

VANISHING WILDLIFE. Roy Pinney, Dodd, Mead & Co., 1963

VOICE OF THE COYOTE. Frank Dobie, Little, Brown & Co., 1949

Index

The Author and Artist

Adrien Stoutenburg is a full-time writer with a varied list of books to her credit, including short stories, poetry, fiction, and nonfiction. Her first volume of poetry, *Heroes, Advise Us,* won the Lamont Poetry Award in 1964. Writing primarily in the juvenile field since 1951, she has produced several novels and is co-author with Laura Nelson Baker of five biographies, most recently *Explorer of the Unconscious: Sigmund Freud.*

A native of Minnesota, Miss Stoutenburg now lives in Lagunitas, Marin County, California.

John Schoenherr has illustrated several animal and nature books for both adults and children, including *Rascal* by Sterling North, *Golden Eagle* by Robert Murphy, and *Gentle Ben* by Walt Morey. A 1956 graduate of Pratt Institute, Mr. Schoenherr lives with his wife and young daughter in Stockton, New Jersey.